P9-CAA-446

Harold Litten's

BEST EROTIC FANTASIES

How to enjoy and understand the sex in your head

FACTOR PRESS
P.O. BOX 8888
MOBILE, ALABAMA 36689

Copyright 1999 by Factor Press. All rights are reserved.
This book or parts thereof must not be reproduced in any form
or medium without the written permission of the author except
in brief reviews.

ISBN 0-7394-1280-9

Illustration by Christian Snyder

To Michael Schmehl
1960-1998

CONTENTS

PART ONE: Your Fantasies and What They Mean

PART TWO: Better Living Through Erotic Fantasy

FOREWARD

Perhaps you remember *The Truman Show*, a film about a man who unwittingly existed in a staged world. The walls he saw were facades. The people he met were actors. Even the sky and sea were artifice. The weather was man-made.

In some ways, Truman is a perfect metaphor for the world of human sexuality in western society. Here's what I mean: From the late 1400's to the 19th century, retarded, deluded and demented women—along with many others who were perfectly normal—were accused of having sex with the devil, were condemned in *church* trials, and executed by the *state*. This was not a localized phenomenon. At various times, more than 100,000 women were murdered for having sex with Satan and practicing witchcraft in Germany, Sweden, England, Scotland, France, Italy, and of course the United States.

Think of it: Not just the ordinary uneducated public, but the church leaders who oversaw the spiritual well-being of the masses teamed up with those who made and enforced the laws to murder innocent women. They "knew" that Satan existed, and "knew" that these women were having sex with him, and, based on that "knowledge," thousands of women were drowned, bludgeoned, or burned at the stake.

From 5,000 BCE (Before the Current Era) until early in the 20th Century, "authorities" insisted that semen contained an individual's life force. (Apparently women had no life force.) If a man ejaculated too many times in a brief period, he actually risked death. If that were true, I assure you I would not be here writing these words. And you wouldn't be reading them. Today we know the nature of semen, the nutrients it contains, the spermatozoa. We know the glands that create its various constituents, those that store it, the organ that propels it. No informed person today believes that a man will die from loss of too much semen, unless he's losing it with another man's wife. But don't laugh it off too lightly: This belief was held not by fringe lunatics, but was "truth" as "known" by the populations of India, China, Japan, the United States, and much of the world.

I've already discussed in *The Joy of Solo Sex* the views against masturbation held by the establishment medical and psychiatric communities even well into the 20th Century. When my father, after getting drunk for the occasion, told me in his own sordid way where babies came from, I asked him point blank, "Is there any other way to get that feeling?" He hesitated, and finally said, "I'm gonna say no. Yeah, there is, but I'm not gonna tell you about it, 'cause if I do and you go ahead and do it, you'll go crazy and your body'll just waste away, and you could even go blind."

True, since 1990, when *The Joy of Solo Sex* was first published, we have, if not buried the taboo against solo sex, at least started digging the grave. We've taken masturbation out of the closet and put it on prime time TV. We've heard with our own ears an Attorney General of the United States suggest that perhaps we should teach it—even if she did get fired as a result. Men are losing their embarrassment about it, joking about it, bragging about it. Both men and women are saying, "I'll do it myself, thanks." Often, they do it side by side.

But don't forget that, less than half a century ago, right here in the real world, we were told that masturbation indicated a character flaw, a frail physique, sexual immaturity, that it would lead to death, madness, physical collapse, blindness, and warts—not necessarily in that order.

At some point between the Platonic era and the Middle Ages of Europe, the Christian Church began emphasizing that homosexuality was evil. That stand led to the passing of laws against homosexuality. As a result, the courts of many nations, including Moslem countries, have sentenced thousands of gay men to death. Hitler arrested homosexuals, forced them to wear pink triangles, and executed many. Even today, laws against homosexual acts are on the books and enforced in some states in the U.S. and elsewhere.

Early in the 20th Century, the psychotherapy establishment declared homosexuality a mental illness, a sexual perversion. Today, that view has been abandoned by the psychotherapy community, replaced by the concept that homosexuality in most cases is a natural and normal result of fetal brain chemistry.

The "reality" of some fragments of the current establishment is that sexual fantasies, along with pornography—which is nothing more than someone else's sexual fantasies recorded in order to be shared—is harmful. Yet, most prehistoric cave dwellers enjoyed sex fantasies, and reproduced them on the walls of their caves. The most sophisticated artists and the most dull-witted adolescents have sexual fantasies. So do grandfathers. (I don't know about grandmothers; I have never had the nerve to ask her.)

Erotic fantasies are as natural as breathing. Most of us couldn't stop fantasizing about sex if our lives depended on it. Although I cannot speak for the female psyche, never having had one, I can assure you that the *average* male under 120 years of age is *obsessed* with sex. From a theological perspective, one might argue that it was intended that way. How else would a scrawny, hairless two-legged beast producing a single offspring every nine months have survived against an Ice Age, a Paleolithic nightmare, a planet brimming with disease? Homo sapiens survived because, when the human male wasn't fending off saber-toothed tigers, running down deer, or trekking off to greener pastures, he was, to put it clearly, fucking his brains out. And when he wasn't fucking, he was masturbating. And when he wasn't masturbating he was *fantasizing* about fucking and masturbating.

I have four goals in this book. One is to show through professional studies just how normal our fantasies are regardless of how "weird" and "deviant" we think they may be.

Second, I'd like to help you fully enjoy those fantasies—indeed, to be proud of and to celebrate your *entire* sex life, however you might choose to express it.

Third, I'd like to help you understand what your fantasies mean, and, through such understanding, to conjure more potent and fulfilling ones.

And finally, I want you to learn how to heal sexual and emotional trauma through the creative use of fantasy.

I have divided the book into two parts. Part I is **Your Fantasies and What They Mean.** Here we discuss the most popular fantasies of all time—or at least in the United States during the last 50 years. Several researchers have actually studied the question, and, although their findings are not in perfect agreement, there's sufficient consensus to establish with some certainty the sort of kinky sex that's going on in your neighbor's head—and your own. We'll talk about the vanilla fantasies of adolescence, sadomasochistic daydreams, imaginary exhibitionism and voyeurism, the popularity of homosexual fantasies even among straight men and women, and even some fantasies that the sexually kinky think are kinky.

In Part II, **Better Living Through Erotic Fantasy**, we'll apply what we've learned about the erotic fantasy lives of ourselves and others to improve both our sex lives and emotional well being in general. We'll learn how others have improved their marriages, healed themselves emotionally, and enhanced their personal sex lives through sexual fantasy. And we'll explore the pleasures of pornography.

Along the way, you will be reading literally hundreds of fantasies, some from men and women who have written to me both in my professional and personal capacities. Some have sought advice, wanting to free themselves from fantasies that, as we'll discover, are perfectly normal. Others simply wanted to share their sex lives with me.

But by far the greatest number of fantasies were submitted by the readers of *CELEBRATE The Self*, The Magazine of Solo Sex. If anyone knows about fantasy, it's the solosexual, the man whose sex life is primarily or exclusively masturbatory. At my request, these men, ranging in age from their early twenties to late eighties, submitted many of the fantasies appearing in these pages. I'm enormously grateful to them for their cooperation and unrestrained honesty.

Other fantasies and their interpretation come from the scores of professional articles and texts cited in the bibliogra-

phy. I'm indebted to this wealth of research. some of it under-
taken by pioneering sexologists and psychologists during a
period when such work required true courage. As for the appli-
cation and interpretation of their findings as well as conclusions
drawn, I take all responsibility.

Here's to feeling good about feeling good.

HAROLD LITTEN
New York City

PART I

YOUR FANTASIES
AND WHAT THEY MEAN

CHAPTER I

Anything...Any Time...
Anywhere

"I first had this fantasy when I was living with Lisa, before we got married," Ron G., a man in his late 30's, told me recently. "We were in our mid-twenties, and had a great, creative sex life together. My birthday fell on a Saturday that year and in my fantasy she told me my present was gonna be sex. Well, that was fine with me!"

Lisa asked him that Saturday afternoon to strip and stretch out naked on the single bed in the guest room. It had no headboard, and she pushed it into the center of the room. Using padded handcuffs on his ankles and wrists, she tied him firmly to the bed frame. She asked him to lift his buttocks as high as he could from the mattress, and slipped several pillows beneath him. That thrust his genitals higher than the rest of his body.

The doorbell rang. Lisa left the room. Several minutes passed while Ron waited with helpless anxiety. Finally, Lisa stepped into the room—nude—followed by three naked men. Ron had never seen them before. Each had bold erections.

"How come you didn't tell us he was this good looking?" one of the men said to Lisa.

"Or that he had such a big cock?"

"Beautiful."

The men approached, and began caressing his body.

"Why are you doing this?" Ron demanded. "You know I'm not queer."

She smiled, brushing his cheek.

Immediately the thin, blond-haired man, probably in his early twenties, knelt between Ron's legs and took the bound man's penis into his mouth. In spite of himself, Ron's organ swelled to full erection.

Lisa and the dark-haired Italian moved to the head of the bed while the third man played with himself. Lisa knelt above Ron on her hands and knees, facing the blond man, her labia inches from Ron's mouth. Then, suddenly, the Italian slid his erection into her vagina, his balls inches above Ron's eyes.

"No, Lisa, don't let him..." Ron muttered, but the phallus continued gliding slowly in and out in rhythm with the mouth on Ron's own organ. Just inches above him, Ron watched the thick penis slip deep into his Lisa, then slide virtually all the way back, pausing, vaginal juices dripping onto Ron's face.

Again, the organ moved slowly into Lisa, the man's scrotum actually resting on Ron's forehead. The genitals above his face took on a life of their own, male and female, moving to the same rhythm, feeling the same pleasure as Ron felt. He began breathing deeply, filling with desire.

He felt the handcuff snap free from his right wrist. His hand was turned palm up, and the huge, rock-hard penis of the third man was laid in it. Without hesitating, Ron wrapped his fingers around it and began pumping.

He heard Lisa moan, then the Italian, and suddenly the third man was impaling Ron's hand steadily. The Italian increased the speed of his pumping, and Lisa backed into him with every thrust. The man between Ron's legs began sucking in earnest.

"Yes, yes," Ron whispered. He thrust himself deeply into the gaping mouth.

Suddenly, he felt the splash of semen on his arm and chest from the organ in his hand. Almost immediately, the Italian withdrew, froze. Untouched, the penis above Ron's face spasmed, ejaculating stream upon stream against Lisa's labia.

"Yes!" Ron moaned as the kneeling blond man expertly masturbated him to orgasm.

Chances are virtually 100 percent that, whether you're male or female, straight, gay, or bi, something in that fantasy turned you on. Why? Because all six of the most popular erotic fantasy types are included in it: the new experience, forced encounters, sadomasochism, voyeurism, exhibitionism, and homosexuality.

Even among adolescent boys, according Robert C. Sorensen, the most common fantasies include:
—Sex with someone who is forced to submit
—Sex with more than one female
—Group sex
—Sex in which the fantasizer is forced to submit
—Various sadistic acts

—Oral and anal sex.

Adolescent girls have sex fantasies too—usually one-on-one with a man they greatly admire. Sometimes there's more than one man, and frequently girls fantasize being forced to submit. They also fantasize mild violence to their partners, and require them to perform cunnilingus·[1]

Alfred Kinsey's findings on erotic fantasy revealed that 60 percent of women have heterosexual fantasies, 10 percent homosexual, and one percent fantasize sex with animals.

A study by Manfred F. DeMartino among women nudists and potential nudists found that the most popular fantasy was having sex with a desirable man. Other fantasies included being raped, sexual contact with animals, group sex, watching other couples have sex, fantasies of penis substitutes, being orally serviced while fellating a man, being a prostitute, and being ravaged by a large penis.

A *Playboy* study showed that sex with a stranger was the most popular among both males and females. That was followed by fantasies of group orgies, someone forcing the fantasizer to submit, the fantasizer using force to get sex, and homosexual encounters. Almost 30 percent of the women and 20 percent of the men also said they fantasized sexual activities that they would never actually practice—and they didn't explain what those fantasies were.[2]

In the May, 1995, issue of *Psychological Bulletin*, Harold Leitenberg and Kris Henning of the Department of Psychology of the University of Vermont, did an extensive survey of the professional literature on sexual fantasies. They reported that finding the truth about the most popular sexual fantasies is anything but easy. For one thing, some researchers present their research subjects with a list of 20, 30—even 50—possible erotic fantasies, and the subjects are asked to rate the ones that are their most common. If their *truly* most common fantasies aren't on the list, they have to make do with what's left. What's more, when asked to list their own favorite fantasies, some people— perhaps most—shy away from admitting what they consider bizarre or sick erotic daydreams.

Still, the researchers say, "There appeared to be four overarching content categories for both men and women: (a) conventional intimate heterosexual imagery with past, present, or imaginary lovers who usually are known to the person; (b) scenes intimating sexual power and irresistibility (including seduction scenes, multiple partners, etc.); (c) scenes involving somewhat varied or 'forbidden' sexual imagery (different settings, different positions, practices, questionable partners, etc.); and (d) submission-dominance scenes in which some physical force or sadomasochistic imagery is involved or implied.... It should be noted that the first category, conventional heterosexual imagery with a past, present, or imaginary lover, is by far the most common."[3]

Other researchers quoted by Leitenberg and Henning found that women also fantasize about sex with a celebrity, seducing a younger man or boy, and sex with an older man. An extensive survey among 4,062 men found that their five most popular fantasizes were the image of a nude or semi-nude woman, sex with a new female partner, replay of a prior sexual experience, sex with two or more women, and the power to drive a woman wild.[4]

Several researchers have found that, among both men and women, "the theme of being overpowered was the second most frequent sexual fantasy reported during sexual intercourse."[5]

In these surveys, the fantasy of being sexually overpowered, or raped, is the thrid or fourth most frequently used by women during masturbation. Others found that "being forced to sexually surrender by an acquaintance," often while tied up was popular. Still other researchers found that 30 percent of their female sample had the fantasy, "I'm a slave and must obey a man's every wish." Another 22 percent imagined, "I'm made to suffer before a man will satisfy me sexually."

A full 13 percent of women said that fantasies of being forced to submit were their favorite.[6]

One of the more interesting studies on sex fantasies—because of the variety it reveals—comes from Canada.

Psychologists at the University of New Brunswick in Canada asked 171 undergraduate students whether they ever had what they called *sexual intrusive thoughts* and found that 84 percent said that they did. The most common of these spontaneous "fantasies" included having sex in a public place, coming in contact with naked people, engaging in sexual contact with someone who is unacceptable because he or she is in a position of authority, and being sexually victimized (both men and women).

These unintended and uninvited erotic thoughts sometimes left the fantasizers uncomfortable; they were not always happy to be thinking along such lines. Yet, here are some of the "fantasies" that bubbled up from their unconscious.(See acompanying chart.)

Erotic fantasies begin in adolescence. Among boys, this is usually at the time of their first nocturnal emissions—11-13 years. Fantasies begin slightly later for girls. These sexual daydreams can be potent stuff.

I was 15 years old when Caroline Fink and I were freshmen at Irvington, New Jersey, High School. She had shoulder-length brown hair, breasts to drool over, the rest of her body perfectly proportioned, a face so lovely I can picture

Sexually Intrusive Thought percentage [7]

	Men			Women	
	n	%	Rank	n	%	Rank
Having sex in a public place	39	67	1	61	55	1
Having sex with authority figure	36	62	3	56	51	2
People around me being sexually victimized	20	35	13	50	45	3
Saying something upsetting to partner during sex	26	46	6	43	39	6
"Disgusting" acts involving genitals	21	35	11	47	42	5
Kissing authority figure	25	43	7	40	36	7
Authority figure being naked	31	53	4	33	30	8
Any other disgusting sexual act	23	40	8	33	30	8
Doing something during sex upsetting to partner	17	47	5	25	23	13
Sexual acts against my religion	22	38	9	17	24	12
"Disgusting" act of intercourse	18	31	14	29	26	10
Forcing adult to have sex with me	22	38	9	24	24	15
Sexual act with "taboo" other	18	31	14	21	19	16
Sexual act with "disgusting" other	21	36	11	26	23	13
Sexual acts against sexual preference	11	19	17	28	25	11
Indecently exposing myself	14	24	16	15	14	17
Sexual act with child or minor	11	19	17	8	7	19
Masturbating in a public place	11	18	19	12	1	18
Sex with animal/nonhuman objects	4	7	20	6	5	20

it even now. We sat next to each other in a couple of classes. That much was true.

The rest wasn't. We went on a picnic in the woods. It was a pine forest in Livingston, New Jersey, not far from Smitty's hack stable. (More about Smitty's later.) She allowed me to undress her completely. She stretched out on a bed of pine needles, her arms above her head, her breasts rising and falling with each breath.

For months I never got beyond that. Just watching her breathe, her abdomen rising and falling, that pert little navel, her eyes holding mine as she smiled softly, seductively—it all hurled me over the edge, splattering my essence against the bedroom wall a foot above the headboard.

During the school year, Caroline and I became close friends. (This is true.) We joined the drama club together and rehearsed our parts. We were both active in public speaking and writing, and it was us against the rich snobs who thought they were so special. We both realized that *we* were the ones with extraordinary talent.

During summer break, I had sex with Caroline regularly in my imagination, and when our sophomore year began, I simply told Caroline how I felt about her. I couldn't go on just being her friend. I loved her.

Turns out she loved me, too. A couple of weeks later we went on a *real* picnic in the woods. I petted her, but it wasn't as good as the fantasy. She wouldn't get naked. I think I was secretly glad. A few weeks later we broke up. That is to say we broke up in the real world. Caroline was still the star of my fantasies. Occasionally I think of her still....

Sex Fantasies Originate in the Unconscious
Their subject matter develops spontaneously—they're

*not pre-planned. Only when they're underway might we con-
sciously choreograph the activity.* In their origins, they reflect
our deepest selves.

Sex Fantasies are Virtually Universal

Psychologist Paul Cameron, Ph.D., writes, "We have
interviewed over 4,000 persons aged 8 to 99 in different situations (at leisure, at work, at home, at school) while engaged in
different activities (ranging all the way from frying eggs to
copulating, to watching a ball game) and asked them whether
'sexual thoughts have crossed your mind in the last five minutes' and 'Was sex or a sexual problem or topic the central
focus of your thought over the past five minutes?'"

To no one's surprise, "Males indicate that sex crosses
the mind about every other minute from the teen years (ages 12
to 17) through young adulthood (ages 18 to 25), then diminish-
es to one minute out of five in middle age (ages 40 through 55),
and then down to one out of ten in old age (65 or older)."

About one time out of five the sexual thought actually
develops into meaningful fantasy.

Teenage females think of sex two out of every five minutes, dropping to one out of three in young adulthood, one out
of ten in middle age, and one out of twenty in old age.
"Obviously," says Cameron, "every thought about sex is not a
fantasy, but some substantial portion of sex thoughts are."[8]

In her book *The Hite Report on Male Sexuality*, Shere
Hite quoted many men who felt fantasies were an integral part
of their sex lives. "Usually, it's very difficult for me to get excited if I'm not thinking erotic thoughts regarding a woman.... If I
think of past experiences of fucking or being masturbated by a
woman, then I become harder and acquire the tension in my
penis that's necessary for ejaculation."

"The use of fantasies is essential to masturbation for me," responds another. "I usually make up semi-elaborate scenes in my head to stimulate me during masturbation." Yet another said he preferred his fantasies to graphic pornography.

"And, as far as thoughts and fantasies I have more than *Yellow Submarine* and *Star Wars* put together. This is what masturbation is all about."[9]

Robert J. Stoller, M.D., sums up the views of most authorities when he writes, "I do not see how fantasy can be left out of one's calculations about human sexual behavior; it is no secret that fantasy, in the form of day dreams, is present consciously in much of sexual activity. In fact, on hearing of a person without sexual fantasy, we suspect that inhibition is in force."[10]

One researcher has written that "sex is composed of friction and fantasy."[11]

We Learn Our Sexual Identities Through Fantasy

There is no question that fantasy helps young people to learn about their sexual selves. That's because, as I've said, the *wellspring* from which fantasy bubbles to the surface is unconscious and spontaneous, undirected and unmanipulated. It expresses truths about ourselves that otherwise we may never discover. Here's an example:

I mentioned earlier that after Caroline and I broke up, I continued to invite her into my fantasies. One involved Smitty's hack stable, where I had begun working on weekends as a trail guide. It was there that I met another guide, Ken, a good looking boy a year younger than I who had curly blond hair and blue eyes and a great sense of humor. We became best friends.

One day when no one was at Smitty's—not even Smitty— Ken took Cynthia and I took Caroline to the barn. We climbed the ladder to the loft, where hay was stored. Suddenly all four of us were naked. The girls lay side by side in the straw. I kissed Caroline's body and watched Ken kiss Cynthia's. Together we mounted our women. We moved slowly. I watched Ken's tight, muscular butt move up and down, and matched his rhythm. We looked into each other's eyes, breaking our gaze only to study each other's bodies. We clasped hands, and, smiling into each other's faces, reached orgasm simultaneously.

Of course you know that never happened. It was an unplanned fantasy that acted out in a "safe" way the sexual attraction that I felt toward Ken. (Coincidentally, 15 years later, Ken and I, with two women who shall remain nameless, lived out that scene in real life—except that Ken and I didn't hold hands. None of that queer stuff for Ken.)

In my mid-teens, I was too young to recognize the bisexual nature of that fantasy. Yet, over time, there were fantasies of men capturing me, masturbating me, fellating me. Even then, I understood that these were *my* thoughts— they were *me*, and I fully embraced and celebrated myself. Uninhibitedly, I allowed my sexual personality to take shape.

According to Warren J. Gadpaille, M.D., most of us deal with all sorts of anxieties and fears through sexual fantasies. For example, many girls and women are so instilled with sexual guilt that they won't even allow themselves to *fantasize* about consensual sex with a man. Instead, they fantasize a romanticized rape during which they're helpless to resist the pleasure they experience. As you'll see, homosexual fantasies among heterosexual men are extremely popular. Even our most violent fantasies, dealing with killing or being killed, can have powerful benefits, allowing us to release feelings of hatred in a relatively harmless way, or to confront our own demise in the arms of eros.[12]

But before taking on such supercharged erotic fantasies, let's look at the basics.

CHAPTER II

Vanilla Dreams

The most common fantasies are vanilla—the kind you can write home to mother about—if you have a liberal mother. Specifically, the single most common fantasies are about sex with a new partner, someone you have never had sex with before, perhaps someone you have never even met until the moment of the fantasy. Or your fantasy lover might be a close acquaintance. Here's an example of a first-time sex experience with a long-time friend, submitted by a *CTS* reader:

> I know a woman about 47 years old named Marge. She works as a night time care giver for elderly patients at a nursing home where I'm the handyman. I'm married with

three children, and I'm just not the kind of guy to fool around, but over the years Marge and I have become good friends, and I think if I asked her for sex she would say yes. Instead, I get off on this fantasy.

One night she asks me, "Luis, can you help me with this problem I have?"

I listen as she explains. "There is this orderly at the hospital who also works nights. I noticed that he comes into the room several times at night and just stands there looking down at me on my recliner with those tight cotton pants that he wears showing everything.

"He's much younger than I am—30 to my 47. But this *stud* has let me know that he'd like to date me."

I say to her, "Would you let him fuck you?"

She says to me: "Yes, that's what he wants. He's offered to take me to a hotel. After all, Luis, I'm off 12 hours. I can afford to give him six."

Me to her: "Go ahead, but protect yourself."

When I see her next, she rattles off an excited story:

"I've had the greatest time. We did go to a motel, stayed for six hours. I'd never done this in the daytime. I'd never had cunnilingus—my husband would never give me that, always straight sex, never variety. My husband never saw my panties. But this *stud* did— held them up in the air and sniffed the crotch, both front and rear. I had worn them at least 12 hours; I'd slept in them. Then he asked me if he could have them. I was almost in shock."

Her gaze dropped to my crotch. She could see that her story was making me hot. My erection was obvious, but I was not embarrassed. I was proud to show her how she affected me. She smiled and then pulled a handkerchief from her uniform pocket.

"It's all right, Luis," she said softly. "Unzip and satisfy yourself."

I did. Not just my penis but my balls, too. As she went on, her eyes went from my penis to my face and back, as though she was talking to both of us. "The last hour or so we spent in the motel room was heavenly," she explained with that enthusiasm. "In the bath, he washed my area and I washed his.

"This man fed me magic, good hot magic. He is absolutely a gentle lover, not demanding, not macho, but gentle as a dove, hard as a bone, large in the right places with a hot and very damp tongue. I can't imagine such masculinity in such a gentle person. He can be a pushover. He speaks softly, but can carry a big stick. Luis, I'm much older than he is. Rooms at the motel are $40 per day. We only use it six hours.

"Oh, Luis, it feels so good, that big thing of his just sliding back and forth, back and forth, rubbing my little button. Oh, Luis, I pull him so tight against my titties..."

Then she just sits there, her mouth open, her face flushed, staring at my cock. I know she wants to reach over, take it in her hand, feel it. But it wouldn't be right. I'm a married man, and she respects me. So, while she watches, I let myself go. As I moan and toss my head from side to side, she smiles and says, "That's good, Luis. That's good."

A 68-year-old professional musician, married and the father of grown children, allows himself to dabble in this most innocuous of gay fantasies:

"My fantasy involves a meeting that I dream will one day happen. Dan, a long-time pen pal, comes to Richmond on a business trip (I select Richmond, Virginia, as the site since I am reasonably familiar with that city). I arrange to meet him at his hotel. I call from the lobby and he invites me up even though I am more than an hour ahead of schedule. Dan had just taken a shower and greets me at the door in a robe.

"What a wonderful moment—he is everything I had dreamed him to be—warm, sensitive and accepting. Instead of a handshake I am pulled into a warm and thrilling embrace. It no longer matters that we have never met—we are unified in that one moment.

"Dan had sent me nude photos of himself, so I was not surprised by his physical attractiveness, but I could not have imagined the depth of his sensitivity to me—a man ten years his senior. Even though I am usually extremely shy, I suddenly want to be free of clothes and to feel his body and my own together. He even assists me.

"Another embrace, then we sit together on the couch—I just want to visually drink this man in. He is sitting at the end of the couch and I lie down, putting my head in his lap so I can look up into his handsome face. My hands trace his facial features; caress his chest and upper torso as we talk of nothing and everything. I can feel a stirring as his large penis swells against the side of my cheek. Turning my head slightly frees his swelling organ, bringing its tip to my lips. As the foreskin reveals the beautiful glans, I kiss the tip, savoring the generous fluid. Wanting to make the experience last, we rise and embrace. I dress, check in and an hour later meet my handsome Dan in the dining room."

This fantasy might well leave you cold, even if you're gay. Yet, for the fantasizer himself, it meets the following criteria essential to a successful erotic fantasy.

I. An Antidote to Boredom

One of the most fascinating characteristics of the human animal is the ease with which it becomes bored. The late radio and television journalist Edward R. Murrow often told the story of a bishop who, addressing students at Yale University, took for his text the four letters, Y.A.L.E. He spoke for no more than five minutes on each letter; yet, when he finally finished, the easily bored students stumbled numbly from the auditorium like the cast from *The Night of the Living Dead*.

As the bishop himself was leaving, he noticed a student in the back pew, kneeling in prayer.

"Bless you, son," said the bishop. "What did I say that has moved you to prayer?"

"I was just thanking God," the student answered, "that I didn't get accepted at the Massachusetts Institute of Technology."

In fact, boredom can actually lead to illness—and suicide. On April 25, 1972, George Sanders, the celebrated actor and veteran of more than 90 films, wrote, "Dear world: I am leaving because I am bored. I feel I have lived long enough." With that farewell, he took an overdose of sleeping pills and died.

Humans require change—any change—on a regular basis. That's what psychologists call The Hawthorne Effect. During the 1920s, Western Electric tried to increase efficiency at its Hawthorne, Illinois, plant. First, researchers varied the amount of light in the plant, then the number and length of rest breaks, and then the length of the work day.

They discovered that increased light led to increased production (decreased light, however, did the same); additional rest breaks led to increased production (fewer rest breaks did the same); and longer work days increased production (you guessed it—shorter work days did the same).

What caused the Hawthorne Effect? A break in the routine, no matter how small. Buy new clothes. Have your hair styled differently. Find something other than television to absorb your attention. Tackle routine chores in imaginative ways.[1]

We *know* that boredom permeates human society. We *know* that it can and does have physical consequences. We *know* that the only antidote is change. We accept that in every aspect of our existence—except one of the most important aspects, our sexuality. There alone, we say, "There's no excuse for adultery/pornography/ masturbation/bisexuality/ etc."

Of course none of us can live up to such an abnormal standard—not even our presidents. So we are driven to hypocrisy. We slink from this fresh, new erotic event to the next, all the while publicly condemning the very activity that we pursue in private.

I don't want to get into the damage done to our self-esteem by consciously playing the roll of hypocrite. I *do* want to make clear that sexual boredom can be enormously depressing. It can destroy relationships. And erotic fantasy is a tried-and-true means of overcoming sexual boredom.

It does that by being *different*. Different from real life. Often, different from previous fantasies. That's the first requirement of a successful fantasy—it must overcome boredom.

II. Subjectively Believable

To be successful, an erotic fantasy must also be believed by the fantasizer. That's not to say that the idea is *objectively* believable. For example, you might not believe that a 47-year-old woman of proper upbringing and having always lived a life of propriety, would suddenly go to bed with a man half her age, then tell another man the details, down to the size and shape of her lover's penis—and finally urge the listener to masturbate to orgasm. The fantasizer himself might find it *objectively* unbelievable. But something akin to autosuggestion takes place here—and I urge you to remember that as we go along. As we found in the previous chapter, erotic fantasy grows out of the unconscious. The unconscious declares, *"This* will turn me on. This mother-figure is condoning my need to masturbate, urging me to have an orgasm, to be happy. She is accepting my sexuality, encouraging it."

To repeat, the fantasy does not have to be objectively believable—it has to be subjectively believed. The typical imagination already knows how to play that game. It will focus intently on the essentials and ignore problematic areas. (For example, are Luis and his woman friend having their talk at the nursing home? Where—in the lobby? Isn't it possible that others will come upon them and discover the man masturbating?)

The reason the man in Richmond is able to reach orgasm simply by putting his lips on another man's penis is that he subjectively believes that it's actually happening. The penis is actually *there*. He can see it, *feel* it, *experience* his lips against the glans. He has never had such an experience in the real world, and the sensation of having it then, for the first time, is all he needs.

A related fantasy is reported by Dr. Edrita Fried:

A particular and not too unusual erotic desire had now come out in the open: Pam wanted to be rocked, bounced up and down and shaken by way of a preliminary genital arousal. And she needed to feel these sensations as part of the body changes and experiences constituting sexual climax. Gradually, as she learned to discover the ways she battled rocking sensations in daily life, she began to face them without shame. And she admitted her desire for such experiences to her boyfriend. Eventually she could reach a sexual climax in intercourse.[2]

III. Involve Control and Power

The third quality of the successful fantasy is also the most controversial: Sex and sex fantasies involve power or control. Although it might be quite subtle, in every effective erotic fantasy, the fantasizer either wields or yields control.

That's obvious in the fantasy of the man from Richmond. He's literally in a submissive posture, his face in the lap of a father figure, all but servicing the man orally. Pam, too, according to her therapist, eventually recalled erotic sensations when being rocked and cuddled as a child by her father. As an adult, rocking restores the sexual pleasure of submission.

But here's a lengthy fantasy in which submission is actually a disguise for exercising great power over others:

In my fantasy, school was out for the day, but I was still in the locker room, showering, because I loved to feel and see the water sensually flow over my naked body, especially my cock and balls. And I liked to do this in the school's shower room most. There it was easy to visualize those swaggering athletic young guys soaping down their naked flesh to wash off the sweat and grime. It made my cock tingle and get big and rubbery just thinking about it. I liked that a lot. In fact, it was the locale for one of my best jack-off fantasies.

All alone, lost in one of my daydreams, I was suddenly confronted with the muscular presence of our school's senior football captain, Bobby Cole. He was standing close enough to touch me, stark naked. The sight made me shiver. But what really blew my cool was his big, hard cock,

He was one big stud, I tell you, and not just between the legs, either. Bobby was all muscle, no fat. Shoulders barn-door wide, huge bulging arms, a massive chest, six-pack abs, a tiny waist, thighs like the mighty oak trunk, a powerful ass that advertised thrusting power, and a cock and balls that left all the school's red blooded American males gasping and drooling in envious disbelief.

He was stroking himself with short, jerky motions while yanking down hard on his nut sack. He was eyeing my stiffening prick so hungrily, I got the giddy feeling that this guy was interested in me.

My cock went rock hard, wild with excitement. It pointed straight up toward the ceiling, dancing and giddily jerking as it throbbed. I thought, I'm gonna cum, and I'm not even touching it!

Bobby suddenly moved in on me. Slapping his beefy dick against my thigh, he slurred through heavy breathing, "Ya wanna be a man, pretty boy? Then suck a big man's cock for a change."

It didn't take me long to decide what I had to do. I fell to my knees, opened my mouth real wide, and started to suck. Man, I tell you it was big! I can't believe the size of that cock. I was just a runt in comparison.

Bobby began to undulate his hips and seriously fuck my face. All the while he was holding real tight to my head. That way I couldn't pull back when his ass drove his battering ram forward. So there was nowhere for that big prick to go but straight down my throat. Now, that was a tough act, initially, but I did it. And with style! That monster cock slid with no problem right past my gag reflex with surprising ease. (That's what's so great about fantasies!)

Horny nuts bounced against my chin, and as his cock slid in and out, a sudden rush of mad, erotic lust grabbed me. I realized that I liked it. I liked sucking cock a whole lot. What had I been missing out on all my life?

Greedily grabbing those musky balls of his with both hands, I chilled to goose bumps at their masculine sexiness. All the while I was slurping and sucking like my life depended on it. Grunts, groans and bull snorts escaped Bobby's throat, telling me he was loving what I was doing.

Suddenly his body tensed. I sensed that he was on the verge of orgasm.

Hunkering down in readiness to shoot their load, those hefty balls of his jumped into action. They rose up on each side of his cock base, and sat there tightly holding on as they jockeyed for the moment to let the semen fly.

Bobby was straining with all his manly might for control. You should have seen him. It was beautiful! His head was thrown way back with his mouth wide open, his eyes were closed, and every muscle in his body was springing into tight, spunk-release mode.

Then it happened! Semen poured non-stop like a river into my throat, as spurt after spurt cannoned out of his wide open cock.

Bobby's growling grew louder than ever, like that of a yawing, wild wind held captive by the forces of the underworld. It came louder and louder until the shower room shook. He trembled, bent at the waist in spasms with each mighty jolt. His straining muscles kept shuddering in helpless bewilderment. Then slowly, inexorably that big beef chunk was reduced to spent gasps, gulps, and twitches.

Here we have an ordinary guy with an ordinary penis reducing the perfect specimen of masculinity to no more than a "big beef chunk," leaving him reduced "to spent gasps, gulps, and twitches." Through his own sexual power, the fantasizer has utterly destroyed the school hero.

To receive an orgasm at the hands (or mouth, or genitals or whatever) of another is to be rendered vulnerable. To *give* an orgasm is to exercise power. I've known both women and men who would rather give orgasms than receive them; they like the feeling of control, and I for one delight in being rendered vulnerable as often as possible: I'm thinking of a bumper sticker pleading, "Please Make Me Vulnerable!"

Both real world couple sex and erotic fantasy can be frustrated when power *can't* be experienced. Dr. Edrita Fried tells of a patient named Howard, who, after six years of marriage, ceased having sex with his wife. They were still very much in love, but, because of a medical condition, the wife could no longer endure intercourse. From Howard's perspective, it had never been a very satisfying experience in the first place, and he happily made the transition into daily masturbation.

His daydream involved an "encounter with some movie star or debutante of whom he had read in the newspapers. The gradual undressing of the woman reached its climax—and he reached his—when he pulled the slip off the girl's breasts."

Howard's sense of power had always derived from seducing women. Only when he could overcome a woman's resistance to his sexual pursuit, get her to say yes and stand naked before him, could he experience the sexual power that led to orgasm. His wife no longer required seducing, and even when they had shared sex it was infrequent and a mediocre pleasure. In fantasy, he could seduce a new woman every night, talk her out of her clothes and into bed, and experience sexual power.[3]

Among married men and women, adultery fantasies are by far the most common. We said that in part they were an escape from boredom. But they also provide another primary satisfaction relating to power: They grant us revenge against the spouse, or punishment—or just allow us to have the last word.

"We've been married for eight years," writes a 29-year-old man from Maplewood, New Jersey. "Her name is Theresa, and we get along real well, except when we argue I might as well just shut up because I know damned well it's gonna be a nonstop full volume monologue from her and I won't get a word in to save my life. That gets me really pissed.

"The last time she shot off her big, fat mouth, I just got in my car and went back to the office. It's my own company and nobody's there at night. I just stretched out on the sofa, still fuming, and then this fantasy came up out of nowhere. Two absolutely beautiful women were all over me. They were naked. One was blonde with really big tits, narrow waist, an ass you could really get your hands on. The other had long black hair, looked a lot like Cher. She was really into cock sucking. They were all over me, with their hands, their tits.

"But here's the part that really got me off. My big-mouthed wife was there, tied naked to a chair, and forced to watch while these beautiful women serviced me."

It's difficult to imagine a more direct fantasy of sexual power.

During masturbation, "an intelligent youth of 16... imagined himself as a 'powerful sorcerer standing on the top of a rock with the whole world at my feet,'" according to N. Lukianowicz, M.D. "A sea of urine was bursting from his penis. It was overflowing and flooding all lands. The patient saw people 'swimming for their lives' in the deluge of his urine, 'and being drowned in the thousands.' He commented, 'They looked like ants, and I felt like a powerful giant.'...The whole picture would end with thunder and an earthquake engulfing the lands and the seas. At the same time the patient would reach orgasm and ejaculate."[4]

Now, there's a power trip!

IV. Celebrate Narcissism

When it comes to erotic fantasy, you're paying for the theater, you're writing the script, you're doing the directing, and you damned well have a right to star in the show. Sometimes, especially among women, actual hardcore sex isn't even present in the fantasy, although it still results in masturbation to orgasm. Here's an example:

"Bella, who had great magnetism, sex appeal, and considerable beauty, wore seductive clothes, and moved and smiled in a manner that attracted many men...fantasized that her attractive home was filled with flowers, that she received the men in the living room, that the time of day was late afternoon, and that she wore a gown that revealed the outline of her breasts. Both she and the imagined male partner were filled with a painful desire for sexual contact. As she moved past the partner he caught her elbow, placed his hand on her breast, and began to kiss her. She could envision merely the pressing of the lips together. Then there was a big blank. While the males varied in these envisioned encounters, the circumstances were almost identical. In actuality, Bella was afraid of and shunned heterosexual contact. She satisfied herself by masturbation."[5]

The following correspondence introduces a critically important point in understanding our own erotic fantasies. On the surface, it describes a man who performs fellatio to orgasm on a stranger. He himself does not achieve orgasm, and the implication is that his pleasure derives from servicing a stranger.

Not so. The fantasizer is very shy, no doubt to the extent that he cannot play the lead in his own fantasies. So he creates an ideal man, as did our locker room fantasizer —but, unlike the earlier dreamer, who conquers the stud through sexual power, this dreamer reverses roles. He identifies with a "very outgoing" young man who is "good looking, had a good build, and his straight-forwardness complimented my shyness."

Here is a classic example of *role reversal* in which the fantasizer services the person he would like to be. The narcissism of this fantasy is apparent:

I unbuckled his belt, unzipped his fly and slid my hand into his shorts to feel everything I was about to see. His big cock-head was slippery and wet. He had oozed considerable pre-cum...a real turn-on for me. Wasting no time, I slid his pants down and had my first look at what was soon to become a very familiar cock and huge set of balls.

His cock was somewhat above average in length, and his cock-head was disproportionately large for its shaft. But very much larger than normal were his *huge*, low-slung balls. Just one of them was a handful. He had recently shaved his ball-sack, so fondling those big beauties was a special treat, and such a turn-on!

Without much delay I slid his dick between my eager lips and moved them up and down his hard shaft. Both hands were busy fondling his big balls. He suggested we get completely nude and head for the bedroom, which we did.

After considerable enjoyment and delight in sucking each other, I told him I wanted him to jerkoff in my mouth. He willingly agreed. Sitting on the edge of the bed with him standing and straddling my knees, his hard cock exactly matched the level of my mouth, and I was quick to suck it in. Holding just his huge cock-head inside my mouth (and his big balls in my hands), he could manipulate the skin of his cock-shaft with his normal jerk-off activity. And I could actively run my tongue fully over his glans. In a very short time I could feel his dick getting harder and harder, bigger and bigger. His stroking became slower and slower.

His orgasm exploded into my mouth. I swallowed excitedly in between deep breaths. He came for 15 spurts or more and I wondered if he would stop. He did of course, but I was not about to take his cock out of my mouth. In fact, when he removed his hand, I took his entire cock into my mouth, massaging it with my tongue and lips until I was sure I'd milked out every drop of his sweet juices.

Not only is the young man who is being serviced an idealized self—he reaches sexually supernatural proportions. His glans is "disproportionately large," a single testicle is a handful, and he ejaculates in 15 spurts.

The most blatant sexually narcissistic fantasy is also rather common and occurs among both gays and straights, males and females. As Porter Davis describes it in *Auto-Erotic Practices,* it is "a completely impossible experience [that] revolves around a female masturbator's desire to engage in intercourse with a man who has only one distinguishable feature, a penis.... Sometimes the subject of the fantasy is merely a trunk of a man, again with a penis. The desire seems to be to create a love-partner with no will of his own, but one whose sexual desire matches exactly that of the woman. This man will act on his own volition, but will do only what the woman desires. This makes it obvious why the man doesn't require a will of his own. The woman is projecting her desires to this image."[6] The man is nothing but penis, totally subject to the woman's power.

Taken to its extreme, the fantasy might be limited to a disembodied penis entering the mouth, anus, or vagina to bring pleasure to the daydreamer. In the real world, dildos serve the same purpose.

We've been talking about vanilla dreams, those fantasies that virtually all of humanity, especially males, have entertained at one time or another. But there is a world of pleasure out there beyond vanilla. For that reason alone it's worth exploring, and the bonus is that you might learn a good deal about yourself in the process.

As Albert Ellis wrote back in 1976: "To masturbate well, then, think your goddamn head off! Don't *desperately* try to get aroused and satisfied; but determinedly and experimentally discover what seems highly exciting to *you* and use that kind of thinking and imagining."[7]

CHAPTER III

My Victim, My Slave

Of the more than 1,000 nonfiction books on human sexuality in my library, approximately one in ten has to do with some form of sadism or masochism, from classics like *Venus In Furs* by Sacher-Masoch to *Sex and Sadism* by Gilbert Oakley, and *Eros and Evil* by R. E. L. Masters. There are books about sex crimes, biographies of de Sade, autobiographies of prostitutes explaining how their customers like to be bound and whipped. There are a few novels—*Story of O, Justine, The 120 Days of Sodom*. And of course there are medical texts like *Psychopathia Sexualis* by Krafft-Ebing, documenting case after case of sadomasochism.

Such books are published because we live in a market economy; people want to buy books on sadomasochism. In fact, no sexual subject is hotter right now than S&M. Virtually all males and a majority of females have had sadistic sexual thoughts and fantasies.

Psychiatrist Walter Braun, M.D., tells of Henri D., whose favorite daydream begins with him driving a "big, flashy car" along a country road. He comes across two young ladies who are hitchhiking. "Both are very good looking. One has a rather innocent face and fair hair; the other girl is a redhead with a permanent mischievous smile on her face. The blond has a firm, robust, healthy figure. The redhead is much slimmer and looks rather like a doll...."

Both sit beside him in the front seat. They strike up a conversation. While he is putting them off their guard, his own secret intentions cause him greater and greater excitement. He decides to take the girls to a secluded castle he owns, but doesn't tell them.

"The two girls are not so cheerful as they were before; they seem uneasy. The redhead is visibly frightened, and the blond, though she tries to bluff, talks too much and too loudly to be feeling really at ease." Once in the building, "The girls are bewildered and helpless." He presses a bell.

"Everything now happens very quickly. I know that any second after this the servant girl will come in. She will be stark naked and there will be livid welts and scars all over her lovely body, the effects of a severe whipping one of the other servants has given her on my orders. At once the two girls will understand what is going to happen to them, why I have brought them here. They will realize that they're about to be seized and stripped and flogged for my pleasure into a state of absolute submission."

That's sufficient for this man. Simply anticipating what's to come stimulates him to orgasm.[1]

In fantasies like this, no sadism actually takes place. Perhaps imposing the fear on the women is what triggers arousal. Usually however, the fantasy must include sadistic acts. Here are some of the more popular:

Bondage and Symbolic Sadism

"In a short time the men were naked, and groveling at my feet, "fantasizes one woman." Now I took golden ropes and swiftly bound each man to a post in the floor, from which he could not stir—so adept was I in the art of bondage. They knew that to resist would be instant death, as I had only to summon a soldier from without, who would enter immediately and put an end to the dissenter with a spear.

"So bound, and helpless, the men gazed up at me as I stood, full height over them, with my sturdy size bared to the hilt. In my hand I held a leather lash—thick handle, the leather tapering away gracefully to a long, cruel end—supple and wicked. I could see already—the men were excited at the sight of my body, for, bound as they were, they could not avoid, save by shutting their eyes, the sight of my revealed body standing over them.

"This pleased me well, as it heightened my pleasure to see these men helpless and bound, yet raised in unrequited lust by their very natures. Then I laid in well with the whip, taking yet another in my left hand to make the pleasure still greater."[2]

Some years ago, I carried on correspondence with a middle-aged marine biologist living in Tampa, Florida. His name was Pete, and he would write such fantasies as these:

"Certainly it would be a fine thing to place you in restraint with balls extended through a small shark jaw, provided with a screw clamp to adjust the bite, and a strap to provide gentle rhythmic traction. This would, of course, be carried out as an indication of my strong admiration and affection, and personal regard, possibly with one of my young muscle stud workout friends as trainee, executing the gentle ball-jacking maneuvers. I wonder if this would appeal to you, among loyal and understanding friends devoted to your welfare."

"In all honestly, though, your photo is very appealing, and I guess my admiration would be best expressed by a few tender applications of the lash to your trim-muscled ass, while stretched against a garage wall in spread-eagle position. I think old pirate practices of whipping at the mast expressed real love of fellow men. Your balls seem to be aching for good leather truss-up, and a little weighted extension. I think most good men need and appreciate a little potent ball work. And a little tit needle work and inward sharp studs on a cock ring would add to your self-realization and complete the picture.... Nailing a guy's sac to a board with a good stout square nail between the balls is also nice."

"But certainly there would be no harm in cleaning your nut sac with a little alcohol, and a good stinging antiseptic, and then driving a shinny ten-penny nail through the sac with one blow—just nail the bag to a plank or a bench so you would have to hold still for further torture because any attempt to move or get away would rip your sac wide open and expose the naked nuts. While you're impaled there, we could give you a little needle work on the tit— just fine little pricks to get you moaning with pleasure, then the insertion of the tit ring. You may not like big hairy men's balls, but that would be best for you, at the moment of penetration of the tit, to have a pair of big blacksmith nuts hung over your mouth so you would have something good and sweaty to lick and chew on while you shot your load."

"I am honored to know that you would trust me to apply the lash and to tie you down—or better, hang you against a garage or dungeon wall, spread-eagled—that's the most tender loving thing I know, to be in total control of a guy's ass and cock and balls, make him confess his sins and fantasies and massage his prostate, and ream that handsome old buddy ass till his cock and balls are sick and dripping to the point he begs you just to cut the fuckers off. Curious thing how a guy often hates his cock and balls and wants them to suffer."

In each of his fantasies, Pete focuses on rendering me helpless. I'm completely at his mercy—he's all-powerful.

But note that, by and large, the sadism is symbolic. I'm bound. Perhaps a single nail is driven through the scrotum—not to harm but to restrain. *I* may move and thereby rip open the scrotum; *I* may beg for castration. Pete's pleasure derives from *power*, not *punishment*. This is *symbolic* sadism.

At first glance, Pete seems to gain no narcissistic fulfillment. The beauty he describes is attributed to the victim. But here's another example of a highly intelligent person creating a role reversal in which he is both attacker and victim. It is *his* body that is being worshipped and abused, his testicles that are the focus of attention.

Here's another bondage fantasy: "Immediately I tie her up, I begin to tremble all over and to feel a great strength welling up in me, a strength I'm totally incapable of feeling under normal circumstances." He describes it as an esoteric, spiritual strength, "a sort of revitalizing of the blood stream, that I feel." He gently whips the woman for several minutes until reaching orgasm.[3]

Writing in *Sex and Sadism,* Gilbert Oakley tells of a teenaged girl who reports, "I twist his genitals. I like that. He cries out. Yet, later, I am all compassion, covering him with kisses, and hardly believe it is possible I could ever hurt a hair of his head."[4] It isn't the brief pain he suffers that she focuses on, but his submission and her power.

Again, to illustrate the need for sexual power through symbolic sadism, is this fantasy of an 18-year-old boy provided by Oakley:

> I tied her hands behind her back, lay her on the bed, and I lash her feet together so that she cannot move. But I never hurt her. I get fun from the fact she is tied like this and watch the appeal in her eyes, see her blushing, listen to her telling me to cover her up and not to look. But the more she pleads the more I am goaded on, until I have torn off all her clothes since I cannot undress her properly because of the bonds around her hands and feet. Then I systematically tear up all her clothes in front of her, and enjoy her anxiety that she will not be able to get dressed again, for her clothes have gone. I then force her to watch me undress, and if she declines to look I pull back her eyelids until she has to keep her eyes open. Then I perform various acts in front of her at which she must look. I release her after—but I have always taken care to have a set of clothes for her to put on, but she has not known this, of course.[5]

Whipping

Human bondage, mentally and physically, says Oakley, "is one of the most urgent and compulsive of sadistic and masochistic inclinations, in both men and women."

But for millions of people throughout the ages, simple bondage and minor whipping have not been sufficient to provide the lustful feelings that lead to orgasm. Wooden canes replaced whips; rods with many thongs or pieces of metal replaced simple canes. In real life, the Russians interwove leather lashes with strands of wire having hooks at their ends. Others created whips with strands of iron. These were not tools of the imagination but of the real world used to publicly flog naked or semi-naked victims bloody ostensibly for the sake of justice, but also to satisfy the sadistic desires of the crowd. It was not much different in its intended effect than the Roman entertainment of throwing Christians to the lions.

In our society—perhaps in *all* societies—we have a discouraging capacity to deny the existence of truths we don't like. If we don't acknowledge it, it will cease to exist. The earth *must* be the center of the universe, or our entire religion will fall apart. People *can't* be naturally sadistic, or humanism is out the window. But we *can* be—and are. And we are also kind, self-sacrificing, and loving.

R. E. L. Masters tells in *Sexual Self-Stimulation* of a 34-year-old happily married mother of two who imagines herself committing the horrible crimes she reads about in the newspapers. She would use her penis (clitoris) to impale the vagina or abdomen of her child victim until "it [her penis] would land in the mass of the warm bowels in the tummy of my prey." Then she would strangle the child, "and this moment, when his body would get limp in my hands, would make me feel the supreme pleasure which I never did experience in intercourse with my husband."[6]

A rather common fantasy among women is strangling their lovers as they simultaneously reach orgasm.

The following fantasy was published in *Confessions and Experiences,* which appeared at the time of Freud and was written under the pseudonym of Cadwe:

I now order Franz to undress entirely and to prepare the whipping bench. Tonight he shall be a real victim! As he realizes my demonical intoxication his excitement rises to such an extent that he cannot hide his shameless passion. I whip him to expunge his rut but he lies down with his member brazenly erect, his hands tied together behind his back, and slowly his tongue starts to play with and caress me. The agile movements of his tongue concentrated on the center of my lust, the knowledge that this creature who makes me undulate in one uninterrupted series of lascivious outbursts is entirely helpless, is unable to satisfy himself in any way whatever, thrill me into a heavenly spasm.

I loose his bonds, tell him to get up and order him, with a command of my hand, to lie down on the wooden bench. He obeys. I fasten his body with leather straps to the bench and stretch his arms and legs until he cannot move.

In a *shameless* way his erect member stands up from his manacled body. Smoking a cigarette, I sit on his face. I don't laugh, I don't show any affection for him. I just rub my body against his mouth letting him feel that he is merely an instrument, a slave to serve his mistress, his goddess.

This time, however, I want more than oral satisfaction, I want the function of his masculinity... But he shall not be a man! His member shall be nothing more than the sheer communication between a powerless and an authoritarian body. I mount him and move. My slave groans; he stammers and utters his confession of dog-like devotion and rut. More and more raging, I dance on this creature. He cannot move, he cannot regulate his lusts. I sense that his climax is imminent and forbid it. His semen shall not ejaculate before I say so. Not to enjoy but just to function is he there. At last I shout "Now" and like a vampire I suck the life-force out of him with jerking movements...[7]

The woman dismisses the man as "nothing," nothing more than "A sexual component..." to be used as a masturbation toy, all the more exciting because he is conscious of being destroyed as a person. The fantasizer is all-powerful, and in the center of her universe narcissistically.

Rape

Rape fantasies are the most common of all among both men and women, and are also popular among adolescent boys, who are usually insecure about both their masculinity and sexual power. "I had no idea how to go about getting a girl to have sex with me," writes one correspondent. "I actually went on a picnic with one girl. We went to a park, and I asked her, 'Well, you want to go for a walk, or eat—or fuck?' She decided she wanted to go home.

"When I got back home, I pretended I held her arms behind her back with one hand, pulled down her tank top with the other, kissed her tits and raped her. It was gentle, and she seemed to like it, and when we were done she said she didn't mind."

That's a typical rape fantasy—no violence, almost willing submission, and sometimes even gratitude on the victim's part. Schere Hite found that many men haven't the slightest desire to actually rape a woman, but as fodder for fantasy, it's close to the top of the list:

"The idea of rape is sometimes a turn-on. I've had rape fantasies. There is a power to sex—a powerful sort of exhilaration."

"I think I have had rape fantasies much in the same sense that women have fantasies of being raped—rather as a mental, excitable concept rather than as a reality."

"Somehow, the animalistic taking of a woman you are sexually attracted to is very exciting to me in fantasy. I wouldn't want to physically or psychologically hurt anyone, though—in reality."

A correspondent writes, "I have this recurring daydream. I'm in a shopping mall, and see a really sexy woman in her late teens or early twenties pushing a cart of groceries across the lot. She's wearing a T-shirt and shorts that show off her jaunty tits and full, round ass. I follow her, and she heads to her car, goes around to the back and opens the trunk. There's nothing behind her but a cinder block wall.

"While she's got her head in the trunk, I come up behind her and say, 'Don't turn around or scream—I've got a gun and I'll use it. Just stay the way you are.' I pull down her shorts all the way to her ankles, and lift her T-shirt up over her head. For all intents and purposes, she's there naked in the parking lot. Then I just pull out my dick, fuck her and walk away." [8]

The narcissism in that fantasy is apparent in the way he relates to his victim. She's merely a masturbation device, humiliated, used and discarded for a moment of his pleasure.

Bodily Harm

Sometimes the fantasies get more violent. A married middle-aged Atlanta businessman with three children writes, "I have this one fantasy that really rings my bells—in fact, it's evolved into several versions. And the crazy thing is, the fantasy itself is gay and sadistic, and I'm neither in real life."

In the fantasy, the man has a teenaged boy chained in the basement. As usual, the victim is naked, fully developed sexually and with mature growth of pubic hair. The man, too, is naked.

He begins by caressing the body gently—the chest, nipples, waist, navel, thighs. The boy's head is bowed, his eyes closed, almost like a crucified savior.

The man weighs his victim's genitals in his hand. Slowly, tenderly, he begins to massage the phallus. It quickly springs to erection, but nothing in the victim's posture changes. The man caresses the boy's abdomen around the navel. Then, without warning, he smashes his fist into the gut.

And so the fantasy alternates from masturbation to powerful blow. The boy throws his head back as the pain from punch after punch surges through his body, neutralized—even overcome—by the pleasure in his groin. The speed of both the massaging and punching increase until finally, with a burst of semen, both the boy and the fantasizer cry out in orgasm.

The fantasizer has entertained many variations on this theme. Sometimes the boy is chained to a table face up and is forced to masturbate himself while the man punches him. Sometimes several men are involved in the pummeling while one of them fellates the young man. There is never any acting out, such as slapping his own stomach. And always when the beating grows so severe as to be life-threatening, the man ejaculates.

I responded by letter, asking this man to conduct an experiment. I wrote, "As you approach climax, I would like you to fantasize that you are the boy, and you cry out, 'Daddy, daddy, please *love* me!'"

He wrote back three weeks later saying, in effect, "At first I didn't want to do it. It seemed sick, stupid—and besides I hate my father. But then I said to myself, it isn't my father, and it isn't me in my fantasy, so what's it gonna hurt? So there I am, a scrawny kid laying naked on a table—I wasn't even chained, just laying there willingly for the first time—pulling on my cock for dear life while this muscular guy stands between my legs and punches me in the gut, first his right hand, then left, then right, then left, so hard I think he's trying to kill me. But it won't stop me from coming. I know I'm coming, getting closer—and that's when I yell, 'Daddy, daddy, please love me, please!'"

Apparently it was the most intense and sustained orgasm the man remembered having. Afterward, he wept.

It doesn't take a psychotherapist to understand what this fantasy is all about. Again, the need for a narcissistic component makes it clear that the fantasizer is identifying with the boy—the center of attention, where the "spotlight is focused." A man (probably his father) is gaining pleasure by harming him. This may or may not have been physical abuse in real life—in fantasy, the punching might represent emotional punishment. In real life, the youth never protested, might even have considered it deserved. Only in the liberating erotic fantasy, in which he and his father are joined in the unity of orgasm, does he find the strength to cry out for love.

Here again we see role reversal. For years this fantasizer believed that he was identifying with the man, gaining erotic ecstasy by pummeling a helpless teenaged boy. Then he allowed himself to face a very painful truth—that, rather than hating his father, he suffered a desperate loss of the man's love.

The sadistic fantasy was an imposter. Where is the spotlight focused? Not on the fists, but on the boy's abused abdomen. It was clear upon first reading that this was not a sadistic but a masochistic fantasy, about which I'll have much more to say in the next chapter.

Now watch how that same fantasy, in the mind of a man identifying with the father, changes the reason the fantasy satisfies:

In the re-cast fantasy, the father is sexually powerful, with a large penis near the boy's mouth or anus. As he pummels the victim, he allows himself to surrender to the youth's sexuality—but only while punishing him for the erotic hold the child has on him. He and the youth will ejaculate together as he lands the final destroying blows.

The destruction can take many shapes. Several underground magazines are devoted to piercing of genitals, castration, dismembering of arms and legs, even heads, so that only torsos remain.

Some years ago I did research on phallic mutilation in fantasy. One man was described to me through communication with his analyst. He was in his late thirties and undergoing therapy to cope with a guilt complex related to homosexuality. He enjoyed pretending that he and his friends had captured a beautiful young man and had strung him like a steer in a butcher shop, by the ankles and with his legs wide apart. His arms were tied behind his back.

One by one, the boys would come up to him and force their organs in the victim's mouth. They would manipulate the helpless boy's head so that, against his will, he would be forced to fellate each of them to orgasm. Finally, the daydreamer himself, a brute of tremendous proportions (in his fantasy) would come forward, thrusting his penis into the boy's mouth and throat. While the boy strove painfully to swallow the enormous ejaculation, the daydreamer would tear the testicles from the young body with his teeth. The climax would come while the boy gagged on the semen and writhed under the excruciating pain of having his organs ripped away.

The description of the victim as "a beautiful young man" might suggest that this is another case of role reversal, but who really is the star of the show, and who the audience? The fantasizer is the one with genitals of tremendous proportions, strutting across the stage to the applause of both his friends and the victim. There's the narcissism. And the power could not be more explicit. While forcing the victim to fellate the conqueror's powerful sex organ, he destroys that of the victim.

Psychoanalyst Richard V. Yazmajian, M.D., reports of a patient, "Abundant fantasies were elaborated of magically acquiring testes; of receiving them as Christmas gifts; and of obtaining them from his emotionally distant father by homosexual submission, chicanery, or direct assault. At this juncture in the analysis the wish for large, powerful testes was expressed in thinly disguised dreams and fantasies. At Christmas season his dreams revealed the most unique transfer of a Christmas wish ever directed toward me—a yearning for a gift of a pair of testes."[9]

As I mention earlier many people fantasize about strangling another during sex. A married woman in her mid-twenties told me that, one night while she was on top during sex with her husband, she put her hands around his throat and began squeezing. He immediately understood the game and did not resist.

"It was just incredible," she said. "His eyes fastened on mine in complete surrender. He knew I was going to choke him to death—his face grew red and blotched. I could hear him struggling for each breath. His dick swelled and throbbed inside me. I leaned forward, rubbing my clitoris hard against the base of his dick. I began kissing his face, but I didn't loosen my grip. I loved him that way, totally helpless, dying. I came three times, then he did, and only then did I let go of his throat."

Although that scene actually took place, with the man free at any time to overpower his wife, it was so enjoyable that both of them frequently masturbate to the recollection of that evening.

I said in the introduction that I wanted to help you understand what your fantasies mean about you. That's particularly intriguing when it comes to fantasies of sexual sadism, whether mild or violent. That's partly because of the great paradox such fantasies present: First, the idealists in our society have been working hard for a long time to equate sex and love. Of course, the equation is minimal at best; some of the best and most satisfying sex has nothing to do with love, and some of the most deeply rooted love has no sexual component. But for those who feel that sex and love are inseparable, the notion that you might get your rocks off fantasizing about beating, strangling, or pummeling the object of your lust simply trips the circuit breaker.

Why, they want to know (and so do the rest of us), do sadistic fantasies increase our lustfulness? All answers are theories only—and there are lots of theories.

According to psychotherapist Walter Braun, M.D., some of us feel isolated and powerless, and, since effective sexual fantasy requires power, the best fantasies for these folks involve dominating, punishing, or even destroying the sex object. Says Braun, the sadist "sees in his partner only an instrument and a tool, an intermediary for the attainment of his goal. Tormenting the partner is not the sadist's one and only aim. Breaking the partner's will is the object he pursues."[10]

But not everyone feels isolated, or sexually powerless. We are not all outsiders. Yet, we are, virtually all of us, in varying degrees sadistic.

Wilhelm Stekel, in *Sadism and Masochism*, blames sadism on Christianity: "The religion of love to one's neighbor inevitably came to grief upon this splitting of love into its two components, spiritual and physical; the first of which was virtue, the second sin, in so far as it could not fulfill its exalted mission, the overcoming of hatred. It led men to deny themselves and to suffer; it gave them pleasure in suffering. Those who suffer become cruel. They envy others the feeling of happiness in life. It builds up a new, secret formula: 'pain for me and pain for you.' Man must become cruel, for he suffers for others. This is the meaning of the conception of savior."

The Pauline notion of a sinful body and a pure spirit has probably caused more psychological damage than any other philosophical concept in the history of the world—with the possible exception of man as superman, as lifted from Nietzsche and applied by Hitler. It is simply a horrible thing to have children be told from the earliest years of their understanding that they were born "in sin" (original sin) and can do nothing about it. ("In sin did my mother conceive me.") And of course when we talk about sin, we mean sex, so that most Americans grow up thinking that their sex drive—or at least the expression of it—is somehow evil. Such conflict among sensitive and predisposed people can lead to perverse acts. They might be as harmless as the practices of the man who wrote to **CELEBRATE The Self** magazine about how he masturbates into Gideon Bibles in various hotel rooms. Or the conflict could express itself in the rape of a pure woman or child—an aggressive attack on the enemy, if you will.

But that is not at the heart of sadism, for the fact is that there were sexual sadists long before there was Christianity, and perhaps before any religion. Probably the truth about sadism was first reported in 1892 in *Psychopathia Sexualis*, written by Dr. Richard Von Krafft-Ebing, a German psychotherapist. He argued that an aggressive character is normal for humans, and that aggression and sex have been related in the human brain—especially that of males—perhaps since pre-human times: "Among animals it is always the male who pursues the female with proffers of love. Playful or actual flight of the female is not infrequently observed; and then the relation is like that between the beast of prey and the victim.

"The conquest of woman takes place today in the social form of courting, in seduction and deception, etc. From the history of civilization and anthropology we know that there have been times, as there are savages today that practice it, where brutal force, robbery, or even blows that rendered a woman powerless were made use of to obtain love's desire. *It is possible that tendencies to such outbreaks of sadism were atavistic.* (Italics mine.)"[11]

The relationship between sex and aggression is *primal,* a hard-wired natural survival instinct to which we probably owe our existence as a species. What if the prehistoric male did indeed take no for an answer? What if he hadn't demanded sex whenever he wanted it? What if he had stepped aside to allow an inferior male of the species to mate with the female, thus creating a reverse evolution in the genetic material? Sex *is* power and aggression. Power and aggression *are* sex.

But in the animal world, both human and otherwise, violence toward the sex object is tempered. In fact, when the object of lust submits, aggression usually ceases to exist. If it did not, the particular species would soon become extinct.

But some humans commit murder in their sexual fantasies, and in real life. That certainly isn't primal. If we're to understand these fantasies and ourselves, we must know why this happens.

Hints of anger that can lead to violence exist in the childhoods of most sexual sadists. They fantasize killing those who have hurt them physically or emotionally. In real life, they're powerless to strike back against their parents, the school bully, or anyone else who has "unjustly" injured them. The internal rage might express itself in cruelty to animals or insects. It most certainly erupts in fantasy. At the onset of puberty, the revenge fantasy merges with the new surge in sexual power and sexual fantasy. Sex revenge fantasies become overwhelmingly lust-inducing.

During the past 30 years, I have met many men who were sex murderers—in their fantasies. They include two lawyers, a doctor, a priest, a truck driver, several businessmen. Some were friends, some business acquaintances, some complete strangers who had read my books and felt they could trust me with what they considered to be a problem. Without exception, they felt guilt and shame at such "sick" fantasies. These were decent men who were contributing to their communities and could not even conceive of really hurting an innocent human being.

Once again: Fantasy springs from the unconscious. It's an honest although sometimes complex expression of who we are. It is unwashed, unadorned and sometimes troubling. Once it reaches the stage of our consciousness, we can utilize fantasy material as a safety valve. We can do "it" without doing "it," and I know of no examples at all in which fantasy has precipitated actual behavior. Rather, the anger buried in the self and *not* recognized in fantasy has *prompted* behavior.

Suppression of fantasy is never wise. As I wrote in *The Joy of Solo Sex*, "Sexual tension will always find release, either through its intended route of coitus or masturbation, or through perversion that may be sexual, or social. It may entail rape or child abuse. It may entail murder, vandalism, senseless violence. But there is no exception to the fact that sexual drive will express itself even if it must masquerade to do so."

Psychotherapy can be expensive. Fantasy is free. It's pleasurable. And it's honest. We do not suddenly become wicked because today we fantasize consciously that which yesterday was still a part of us but buried in the unconscious. The only difference is that today we are self-aware.

Now let's examine the flip side of sadistic fantasy.

CHAPTER IV

The Joy of Surrender

In his great work *Faust*, Goethe writes this description of the joy some find in suffering:

> Endless ecstatic fire,
> Glow of the pure desire,
> Pain of the piercing breast,
> Rapture of God possessed!
> Arrows transpierce ye me,
> Lances, coerce ye me,
> Bludgeons, so batter me,
> Lightnings, so shatter me,
> That all of morality's

Vain unrealities
Die and the stars above
Beam but eternal love!

More mundane by far but equally to the point is this exchange between a sadist and a masochist:

Masochist: "Please, please, beat me, punch me, whip me, abuse me!"

Sadist: "No."

Nineteenth century novelist Leopold von Sacher-Masoch wrote the novel *Venus in Furs*, in which the lead male desired himself "completely and unconditionally subject to the will of a person of the opposite sex, and being treated by this person as by a master, to be humiliated, abused, and tormented, even to the verge of death."[1] Sexologist Krafft-Ebing read the book, and was the first to call masochism masochism. Precise definitions have been elusive, however. In strict psychoanalytic terms, masochism has been described as "the suffering of physical pain as a prerequisite to orgasm." [2]

But the masochist doesn't actually "suffer" pain. Sometimes there's no pain to suffer—the cruelty may be psychological. The "victim" might merely be restrained or humiliated. Or the whole experience might be nothing more than fancy; The imaginary victim might be maimed, burned, drawn and quartered, and still not suffer the slightest scratch.

What most experts do agree on is that masochistic fantasies are extremely common. Theodor Reik has written, "There is no doubt that the instinct of masochistic inclination is widespread. Thousands of persons have confessed that they are acquainted with such sexual enjoyment. Most of them have revealed further that this is the only sexual pleasure they know.

How many more there must be who could say the same thing, but keep silent!"[3]

Freud went even further, claiming that masochism is "the most frequent and most significant of all perversions."[4]

The reason masochism is so hard to define, and also so common, is that it's amorphous. Does the idea of getting bound tightly in ropes, leather or rubber while someone masturbates you seem exciting? How about being tied to a chair and forced to masturbate yourself while people jeer? Does your most potent fantasy include being beaten or spanked? How about being forced to perform cunnilingus or fellatio—or being raped? How about suffering castration or having needles pushed through the glans of your penis? One of these fantasy ideas might well push all of your lust buttons while the others leave you cold. Yet, each is masochistic.

Masochistic fantasies have these characteristics in common:

The Absence of an Actual Pain Experience

I can illustrate this best by an extreme example written by the famous Japanese author Yukio Mishima. This is from his short story "Patriotism," in which a man commits hara-kiri:

"By the time the lieutenant had at last drawn the sword across to the right side of his stomach, the blade was already cutting shallow and had revealed its naked tip, slippery with blood and grease. But suddenly stricken by a fit of vomiting, the lieutenant cried out hoarsely. The vomiting made the fierce pain fiercer still, and the stomach, which had thus far remained firm and compact, now abruptly heaved, opening wide its wound, and the entrails burst through, as if the wound, too, were vomiting. Seemingly ignorant of their master's suffering, the entrails gave an impression of robust health, and almost a disagreeable vitality as they slipped smoothly out and spilled into the crotch. The lieutenant's head dropped, his shoulders heaved, his eyes opened to narrow slits, and a thin trickle of saliva dripped from his mouth."

No question, that's a brutal, excruciatingly painful masochistic fantasy (Mishima often indicated that he was a masochist). Yet, in that entire passage, we read only that the vomiting made the fierce pain fiercer still, and that the entrails were ignorant of their master's suffering. This fantasy isn't about grotesque torture. The pain, rarely fantasized in detail, is a necessary incidental which leads to an essential part of the fantasy.

Surrender

What is required of the masochist is submission. And remember this: The more passive he becomes, the more accepting of his fate, the greater the sexual excitement. A sadist, for example, might want his fantasy victim, whom he is strangling, to fight violently until the last gasp. That same fantasy in the mind of a masochist has him surrender to his fate while in the throes of orgasm. Surely he might kick and fight violently during the "setup" part of the fantasy, but when the erotic enters, he must surrender.

Dissolution

In the second part of this book, where we talk about improving the intensity of our fantasies, I'm going to have a lot to say about dissolution, the fading away of your self- awareness. It's why some people drink alcohol or do drugs. We realize that now and then we need a vacation from ourselves. Technically, what we're escaping is our own neocortex, that part of the brain that reasons, thinks, is self-aware. Arthur Koestler in *The Ghost in the Machine*, has described the development of the neocortical part of our brain as an evolutionary mistake.[5] It so dominates our being as to virtually suffocate much of our primal existence, and that is nowhere more in evidence than in the realm of our sexuality. In all sexual fantasy, we seek to eliminate neocortical influence, to reach a plane of intellectual dissolution. The masochist does that by raising a competing distraction to consciousness—the whip or other punishment—until nothing, not even the abuse, clutters the mind, opening the door to joyous, overwhelming lust such that even the pain is overcome. Even the fantasy of sex and death hinges on dissolution of self, the simple surrender into orgasm and oblivion.

Narcissism

I've said that narcissism is essential to successful fantasy. Notice as you identify with the masochist how narcissistic is his experience. *He* is restrained, all eyes upon his suffering. *He* is bound and beaten, his audience spellbound by his gyrating body, phallus erect. *He* is being strangled, the eyes of his destroyer fastened on the overwhelming beauty and sensuality of the heaving, spasming body and pelvic thrusts. The dissolution is into lust, yes. But it is totally narcissistic lust.

It climaxes in what Theodor Reik and the Marquis de Sade in his role as masochist both describe as far more intense sexual pleasure than most people ever know.

Those are some of the qualities that all masochistic fantasies share. Beyond them, the actual act that brings pleasure can vary dramatically. At its most mild, the masochistic fantasy might involve bondage, humiliation or both. Following are some of the most common masochistic daydreams, progressing from the mild to the violent.

BONDAGE

"He dreams of watching a stubborn girl abducted by a slave gang," writes Earl Harper in *A Study in Masturbation Fantasies*. "She is tied to a board; her wrists are bound. Her legs are spread far apart. Now, other girls are seen tied and bound in a similar manner. A few men start fondling and then tickling the exposed female genitalia. The stubborn girl squirms nakedly while enduring such humiliation. The patient watches, feels exhilaration, an erection, and an orgasm."[6]

You might think that's a sadistic rather than masochistic fantasy, but what exists here, according to Harper, is a role reversal: "This...fantasy reveals masochism and transvestism because the patient regards *himself* to be the stubborn bound girl and the humiliation is most stimulating."[7]

But there may be a lot more than humiliation at stake here. When I was in my mid-twenties, an artist friend of mine offered to draw a sketch of me nude in any pose I chose. I selected the one below, asking him to add the restraints. The picture still hangs in my office, handsomely framed. The plate on the frame carries the title: "Freedom."

Among the few people who have seen the drawing, some have remarked that the name is a paradox. But it's only apparently so. The man in the picture is naked, vulnerable, and helpless. He is available for any sort of sexual use anyone wants to make of him, whether to impale him orally or anally or to fondle, or masturbate him. That's the attraction of bondage. Yes, it can be humiliating to have your body immobilized in a position that exposes your anus and genitals obscenely while you, bound and helpless, can do nothing about it. But, at least as important, you are helpless to prevent yourself from being pleasured sexually. You can do nothing but surrender to being used, abused, and brought to orgasm. You are *free* to be totally and exclusively sexual.

"Freedom," by Allen Metzgar

HUMILIATION

A man imagines himself a 14-year-old boy who sits naked in the middle of the living room surrounded by relatives fully clothed, young and old, while his mother harangues, "Go ahead, play with your penis the way I caught you doing this morning. Show us all your filthy little habit. You can't do it, can you?" But in fact he can. His potency triumphs over their condemnation and the humiliation they cause him as he splashes his semen all over his audience. In that fantasy, the masochist has victory over his tormentors, but in many humiliation fantasies, there's no such obvious triumph. One of the more curious examples of this comes from real life. In several cities gay bars exist with back rooms that contain tubs in which men will lie naked while others urinate and sometimes defecate on them. Here is the ultimate humiliation—most people wouldn't treat an animal in this fashion. Being so degraded, in fact or in fantasy, sets the victim free to feel lust.

SPANKING

The world abounds in literature, drawings, photographs and videos devoted to spanking in a sexual context. The majority of such material appeals to men responding to the fantasy of spanking a woman, but Kerry and Jack Novick, both psychoanalysts, describe a woman who had masochistic spanking fantasies. "Mrs. S. described a beating fantasy which she used in order to achieve orgasm. In the fantasy she imagined her father telling her that she was bad, putting her across his knee, and spanking her. She only became conscious of the fantasy just before orgasm, and then habitually forgot it again."[8]

One man reported, "I have this sick fantasy of lying on a board with a hole in it and my cock of course through the hole. I'm being whipped by my father, and every time the blow falls, I jerk forward into the board. After a while two things happen. I surrender to my helplessness, my submissiveness to this man who is all-powerful. And that surrender to his brutality firms me up. 'Look at me,' I say to him. 'Look at my cock, Dad!' And at that moment I shoot."

A man responding to Shere Hite's survey reported, "I love to get a good hard whack on the ass while I am fucking her. The harder the better, and I like it if it just grazes my balls, or it can even hit my asshole. I feel it all the way through to my cock, or the base of it inside the skin. It makes it feel like a fire is there."[9]

Leon Ferber writes, "Beating fantasies are probably universal, present in the life of every person..."[10]

Ferber tells of a woman who, in fantasy, was first humiliated by a cruel man, then spanked by him on her bare buttocks. Another imagined that a tough, sadistic young man punched her repeatedly. The fantasy would be even more likely to lead to orgasm if she could visualize him in tight blue jeans and black boots.

Ferber once had a male patient with a beating fantasy that took a really confusing route to satisfy his sexual needs. And it was the *only* way that he could achieve orgasm. In his imagination, a young girl is bound naked. A voluptuous woman wearing boots beats the child. While the girl suffers, the man masturbates to orgasm.

Ultimately, the patient's protective defenses were stripped away. The girl was not a girl at all but the patient himself as a child. The woman provided a safe, heterosexual way for the patient to accept that the father was beating the child. And finally, the beating was not a beating: "The central meaning was a wish to be beaten by the father, which stood for passive sexual yearning for him. The patient came to recognize that he "not only admired his father and loved him, but also feared him." Ferber concludes, "The infantile wish to be loved genitally by the father is probably regularly conceived of as being beaten by him."[11]

Solo sex might have been a great deal more rewarding for this man if he had just been able to be honest with himself. Why *not* fantasize that his father, whom he hated, had tied him naked and forced the helpless child to satisfy the man's lusts? Might he not have made the most thrilling of all discoveries—*self*-discovery, self-understanding? Few experiences are more empowering and healing than eroticizing and confronting in ecstasy our greatest fears and shames. Eros demystifies, desensitizes, objectifies. We *can* deal with problems that we have turned into orgasms.

Edward D. Joseph, M.D., reports in the monograph *Beating Fantasies* of a woman who fantasized "hanging by my thumbs stretched from head to toe, beaten but never killed. Later, she revealed these were concentration camp fantasies: "....A man or a few men with sadistic eyes strapped me down to a table with the ideas of beating or torture...there was a lot of sexual stuff too, but kind of mixed up." Sometimes she would be masturbated either by hand or a machine, and would become so aroused that she would be "dying from it." Occasionally, instead of being tied to a table, she was bound to a stake, and the fantasy involved many men "using her."[12]

To appreciate masochistic fantasy we need to know something of its popularity in real life. Indeed, masochism has been around for a very long time. In ancient Greece, the Lacedaimonians celebrated a Day of Flagellations, during which boys voluntarily submitted to being beaten before the altar of Diana. Plutarch wrote of the festival, "Boys are whipped for a whole day, often to death, before the altar of Diana and Orthian; and they suffer with cheerfulness, and even with joy: nay, they strive with each other for victory; and he who bears up the longest time, and has been able to endure the greatest number of stripes, carries the day."[13]

Mass flagellations also occurred in Syria, Rome and Egypt. Herodotus reported that Egyptian priests often whipped each other while making sacrifices to a goddess. At times, the entire assembled population of several thousand beat one another.

A monk of Saint Justina in Padua reports of mass flagellations throughout the population of Italy:

> When all Italy was sullied with crimes of every kind, a certain superstition hitherto unknown to the world first seized the inhabitants of Perusa, afterwards the Romans, and then almost all the nations of Italy. To such a degree were they affected with the fear of God, that noble as well as ignoble persons, young and old, even children of five years of age, would go

naked around the streets without any sense of shame, walking in public, two and two, in the manner of a solemn procession. Every one of them held in his hand a scourge made of leather thongs, and with tears and groans they lashed themselves on their backs until the blood ran; all the while weeping and giving tokens of the same bitter affliction as if they had really been spectators of the passion of our Saviour, imploring the forgiveness of God and his Mother, and praying that He who had been appeased by the repentence of so many sinners would not disdain theirs.

And not only in the daytime but likewise during the nights, hundreds, thousands and tens of thousands of these penitents ran, not withstanding the rigour of the winter, about the streets and in church with wax candles in their hands, and preceded by priests who carried crosses and banners along with them, and with humility prostrated themselves before the altars. The same scenes were to be seen in small towns and villages, so that the mountains and the fields seemed to resound alike with the voices of men who were crying to God.[14]

The fakirs of India practically flailed themselves bloody, and Saint Dominic, early in the 13th century, helped improve the efficiency of self-flagellation. "He taught Flagellators to lash with both hands, and, consequently, to do double execution. One could thereby remove twice as much skin from his back, and discharge twice as much useless blood from his veins. He [Dominic] obliged the world with the invention of knotted scourges. This discovery, also, facilitated the flaying of the shoulders, and enabled a skillful hand to mangle the flesh in fine style for the good of the soul."[15]

Maria Magdelena of Pazzi, a Carmelite nun of Florence in about 1580, was a committed masochist. It was her greatest delight, according to John Swain, "to have the prioress bind her hands behind her and have her whipped in the naked loins in the presence of the assembled sisters. While being whipped her thoughts were of love and she frequently cried out, 'Enough! Fan no longer the flame that consumes me. This is not death I long for; it comes with all too much pleasure and delight,' etc. Elizabeth of Genton, another flagellent, used to cry out under the discipline, 'O love, O eternal love, O love, O you creatures! Cry out with me, love, love!'"[16]

Yet another example, this one from Theodor Reik: A 25-year-old man feels a strong sexual excitement which he attempts to master. Therefore, he undresses, goes to his mirror, where he sees himself naked. He whips himself on his buttocks with a dog whip until bloody weals appear—while constantly looking into the glass over his own shoulder. During this the sexual excitement increases until finally ejaculation occurs. *The sight of his own blood is the signal for orgasm.*"[17]

Rape and Forced Sex

"I've often had fantasies of being raped by a woman," a man told Shere Hite. "A group of aggressive feminists catch me in an armlock at the foot of the stairs and proceed to feel up my crotch and squeeze my ass, saying, 'How do *you* like being treated as a sex object.' (Well, it's a nice fantasy anyhow.) Personally, I feel that female rapists ought to get government grants. (But there should be the death penalty for a woman who just teases you.)"[18]

Almost all of us, regardless of gender or sexual orientation, have had fantasies of being used for sexual pleasure without our cooperation. It fills the requirement for narcissism in that the attacker is fully absorbed in the beauty and sexuality of his victim. And it is that victim who, by virtue of his or her sexual attractiveness, causes the attacker to cast aside every remnant of civilized behavior to fulfill the lust the victim engenders.

In 1969, Manford F. Martino, in the book *The New Female Sexuality*, presented interviews with 175 female nudists, "potential" nudists, and lesbians. He asked, "What is your reaction to the thought of being raped, in a nonviolent but forceful manner?" He made it clear that in the fantasy there were not to be any threats of bodily harm. Fully one-third had positive reactions. Some were downright ecstatic.

Once again, masochistic rape fantasies, like other forms of sexual masochism, are often attributed to sexual guilt and shame. Wilhelm Reich, a student of Freud, has written, "This passive rape phantasy in the woman...serves no other purpose than that of alleviating her guilt feelings. The neurotic women can engage in intercourse without guilt feeling only if—actually or in phantasy—they are raped, thus shifting responsibility to the man. Formal resistance of many women in the act has the same meaning."[19]

These "attacks," of course, are almost always romanticized and nonviolent. Here's a detailed example of forced oral sex involving a gang and a gay man. In real life, this would be a brutal and perhaps life-threatening experience.

My name is Jake. I'm 45 years old, and a substitute school bus driver. I might add that I can pass for a 25-year-old stud in most situations.

The route that I drive starts nine miles from town. So the bus is parked in a garage at night not far from where I live and work at my regular job. I've lived here all my life, so I know most everybody, and everybody thinks they know me...generally.

Clyde, a big, handsome jock, is the first to get on the bus in the morning, and the last to get off most every day, unless he has a game or practice. I've known him all my life, and he has grown into a hunk of drop dead masculine beauty. When I sub, I can't take my eyes off him from the moment he enters the bus until he leaves. He always stops right in front of me, so his big crotch bulge is just inches from my face. Then, he moves loosely up the aisle to his seat, deliberately emphasizing first his right and then his left butt cheek as he walks.

He'll turn and step off the bus in the same provocative manner.

After I garage the bus, I am required to clean it out for the next day. The days Clyde rides home, I know I will, with pounding heart, find a pool of shimmering semen on the floor, and a seat that, when I rub my nostrils across it, smells of male testicles where Clyde sat on his bare ass jacking off just moments before. The smell of that intoxicating odor always drives me into a sexual frenzy. I get a hard boner, and my head seems to blow up real tight with a throbbing pain around my eyes. Then I drop to my wobbly knees, and ecstatically rub on my own dick.

That's what I'm doing now in my fantasy, when, without warning I'm surrounded by four well-muscled, bare-assed naked young bucks, all ramming their erect phalluses in the air while holding them tight in their fisted grasps. They're steadily grabbing and pulling at me, ordering me to "get to gobblin' any dick that finds your horny mouth, ya fuckin' wimp!"

It's Clyde in all his sweet-smelling, sweaty dazzle that I taste and gobble first. The shivers of ecstasy of that first moment when I look him hard and full in those flashing eyes of his, I feel I must be dreaming because I can't even think without getting all light-headed. Ain't ever sucked a cock before and here I am munching on a hunky beauty's prick.

Meanwhile, the three other cocks are thrusting and spasming pre cum in my hands, ears, and eyes, and rubbing and sliding it luxuriously over every inch of my face and neck. The thick, spunky smell of semen and breath-taking cock essence makes me gasp.

Without any warning, Clyde closes his eyes, stiffens, gasps spastically, grabs at my head, and spews his stud seed lustily in thrusts down my throat.

The relentless grunting, shoving and fondling of rampant cocks continues unabated, while the testosterone-crazed studs jockey again for my mouth. Clyde pulls his throbber free of my jaws, and immediately a new, over-stroked dick begins to probe the depths of my throat.

To my surprise and delight, this cock's different tasting, kinda sweet, not near as acid as Clyde's. My eyes open to discover that it's sexy Niki. He's the town lover boy with the heavy, sensual lips, and scandalous bubble butt, and he's blasting torrid loads of sexy looks at me with those sparkling blues of his. Now I know why the gals and guys all love him so much. He's slick, smooth, and never rough or jerky. His heavy, salami cock actually caresses my mouth as his gentle butt thrusts, and his eyes are absolutely devastating.

He comes too fast, breathes heavy in intense, short, sexy bursts through wide-flared nostrils.

While Niki slowly draws his thick pecker out of my mouth, Charlie, the youngest of the hunks, moves in, mounting my face as he rams his light-weight cock deep in my mouth. He lets out a long, loud moan as his short, quick spurts drain his tight balls almost instantly. I never get to see his eyes....

The last cock of the four young hunks fails to find its mark, and just wildly spurts all over my face—some in and some out of my mouth. Vinnie, a guy I've never seen before today, is jerkily handling his short, stubby dick as he attempts to get some special joy out of his disappointing ordeal. He shields his embarrassed eyes and looks away.

But the fantasy doesn't end there. The men proceed to strip Jake naked. Jake writes, "They don't know it, but I'm slowly entering a state of deep euphoric ecstasy, and whatever they do now is only driving me higher and higher toward the eventual sexual release epiphany." They abuse him verbally, while "I shiver with an uncontrollable, sharp, emotional, breath suck-in. The hunks become cock-obsessed studs." They proceed to service their victim. In this fantasy it's particularly obvious that the "victim," through the direct power of his sex organs to induce lust in others, is the one in control. (More about this fantasy in the following chapter.)

Castration and Phallic Mutilation

Few people have any idea how much diversity exists in the realm of sexuality. For example, some of you may ask, "Why include such a bizarre category as castration fantasy?" On the other hand, others might actually subscribe to *Katharsis*, *Enigma News*, or have copies of the now defunct *Noose Letter*, Larry Townsend's *Treasury of S&M* or the enumerable other publications devoted to genital torture and castration in particular. The chances are you yourself have had fantasies in which you were either mutilating someone sexually or being mutilated. No doubt you thought it was an incredibly sick thing to fantasize, and unique to you. In fact, it isn't rare.

Not long ago, a young man told me in a letter of a fantasy in which he was taken prisoner by a gang of leather-jacketed young hoods. They stripped him, hung him from a tree, his hands tied firmly behind his back, and beat him with their fists until he was a mass of bruises. Then each of them kicked the youth as hard as they could in the testicles. They left him bleeding, his bones broken, and in great agony. He often masturbated to this fantasy, and reached orgasm while the sadists were kicking his genitals.

To add realism, he sometimes squeezed his own testicles until they ached. He associated this minor pain with the kicking.

A variation of this idea was that the men, after chaining him, pulled switchblade knives from their pockets. While he watched helplessly, each came up to him and plunged their blades into his scrotum. When the last of the gang sliced his sac, and he, in his imagination, gazed down on his mutilated balls dangling from their cords, his ejaculation came.

Reik gives more examples of mutilative fantasies. One is that of a 37-year-old father of three children:

"To an ancient barbaric idol, somewhat like the Phoenician Moloch, a number of vigorous young men are to be sacrificed at certain not too frequent intervals. They are undressed and laid on the altar one by one. The rumble of drums is joined by the songs of the approaching temple choirs. The High Priest followed by his suite approaches the altar and scrutinizes each of the victims with a critical eye. They must satisfy certain requirements as to physical beauty and athletic appearance. The High Priest takes the genital of each prospective victim in his hand and carefully tests its weight and form. If he does not approve of the genital, the young man will be rejected as obnoxious to the god and unworthy of being sacrificed. The High Priest gives the order for the execution and the ceremony continues. With a sharp cut the young men's genitals and the surrounding parts are cut away.

"The patient, who is of a decidedly visualizing type, imagines the progress of the scene very vividly. He himself is not a participant but only a spectator." According to Reik, "the daydreamer identifies with one of the victims, usually not the one who is just being castrated but with the next, who is compelled to look on at the execution of his companion. The patient shares every intensive effect of this victim, feels his terror and anxiety with all the physical sensations since he imagines that he himself will experience the same fate in a few moments."[20]

Another patient's fantasy centered around an English officer who had been captured by an ancient tribe of Aztecs. The tribe periodically sacrificed their prisoners to their gods by solemnly castrating them. "Until the execution the prisoner is a guest in the house of his captor who is also supposed to carry out the sacrificial operation. One day he takes the officer—who otherwise is treated very kindly—into a room in order to show him the genitals of previously castrated men."[21]

Reik says that the daydreamer struggled over the question, "Just where and how are the genitals preserved?" Originally the daydreamer was satisfied to have them stored in a beautifully carved chest, but the decaying and shrinking process which would naturally occur made this unsatisfactory. He also rejected the idea of stuffing and displaying them as dead birds are. "Finally the daydreamer decided on having them preserved in bottles filled with alcohol," Reik says. (Remember that a successful fantasy must be *believed* while it's being imagined.)

Another of Reik's patients fantasized that "several naked young men are exhibited in the slave market and are sold to women, chiefly older widows. When these slaves are brought to the homes of their mistresses and refuse to satisfy them sexually, they are castrated."[22]

Sexologist Krafft-Ebing tells of a middle-aged married man who found satisfaction for many years in the fantasy of a beautiful woman stabbing and cutting his genitals and perhaps killing him with knives. The researcher says that this case can be compared with numerous ones in which men find sexual pleasure in being lightly pricked with knives in the hands of women who, at the same time, threaten them with death.[23]

The most prolific writer of masochistic fantasies involving genital mutilation is the Marquis de Sade. His sadomasochistic

The One Hundred Twenty Days of Sodom is itself a massive, unrestrained fantasy. In it, Sade reveals his preoccupation with the phallus, its size, use and abuse.

Early in the book, he reveals his obsession with the male genital member. He concocts the idea of supper parties in Paris. In his imagination, they are attended by 16 young men, from 20 to 30 years of age, each with an immense sexual organ.

"The youths were selected solely upon the basis of the size of their member," he writes, "and it almost became necessary that this superb limb be of such magnificence that it could never have penetrated any woman; this was an essential clause, and as naught was spared by way of expense, only very rarely would it fail to be fulfilled."[24]

Sade, speaking through the character of a female prostitute, describes a customer "whose buttocks and thighs, member and balls had to be pricked with a golden needle. Not until he was covered with blood did he discharge. I handled that commission myself," says the prostitute, "and he constantly shouted to me to thrust deeper. I had almost to bury the needle in his glans before seeing his fuck squirt into my palm. As he unleashed it, he thrust his face against mine, sucked my mouth prodigiously, and that was all there was to it."

Another customer, according to the same woman, had his "buttocks, belly, balls and prick stabbed with a heavy cobbler's awl."

"Another," according to the whore, "carried, in a small pocket case, a little knotty stick which he kept for an unusual purpose; he wanted me to insert the stick into his urethral canal, and, having plunged it in to a depth of three inches, to rattle it with utmost vigor, and with my other hand to pull back his foreskin and frig his poor device." Another customer demanded that she take a burning candle and hold it over his sex organs so the hot wax fell on them. Although no touching was required, "before they would yield fuck, his genitals had to be given such a heavy coating of wax that toward the end there was no recognizing this strange object as a part of the human anatomy."

The shedding of blood plays a major role in the later fantasies of Sade. A young man is first whipped, then raped anally and finally castrated. As Sade's passion for mutilation increases, so does the sordidness of his fantasies.

Terminal Fantasies

In his book *The Breathless Orgasm*, John Money describes this fantasy: "In tenth grade, I masturbated for the first time with fucking in the fantasy. But it was a fantasy of boys who I knew in school fucking me. I would imagine that they would gang up on me, rape me, and then would strangle me. One would strangle me with his bare hands and two others would hold down my arms so I wouldn't fight back. Another one would be on his knees playing with my sex organ. Then they would pull me into a standing position with my pants and underwear down. The orgasm came when I was strangled to death."[25]

Even as a child, this man practiced autoerotic asphyxia. In his fantasies, he always ended up dead. "I would pretend that I was fighting and struggling in front of the mirror while I imagined a homosexual lust murderer was strangling me—someone like John Wayne Gacey," he told John Money. In reality, "I strangled in front of the mirror, my beautiful butt and legs struggling as my face turned red until I couldn't hold my breath anymore, and I fell to the ground. After the murderer (me) masturbated my penis, I put the underwear and dance tights away in a special place and would sit and wonder why I do it."

He fantasized being a disco dancer who would walk home at night still wearing his fancy suit. Suddenly a bunch of boys would "gang up on me and strangle me. My penis could be seen through the tights, and my pelvis struggled until the orgasm came with my last gasp. My mouth was wide open and my tongue stood way out until it folded back and disappeared when I died.

"A hangman's noose would come down from the ceiling, grab hold of my neck, and pull me up into the air as if the rope were connected to a pulley. I would struggle in mid-air and my beautiful buttocks and penis could be seen through my tights as my pelvis lurched madly. Soon I would strangle to death and at the final gasp, the orgasm would come. Finally, the hangman's noose lowered my dead, sexy body to the floor. My eyes were frozen open."[26]

In *Sun and Steel*, Yukio Mishima describes a related compulsion: "Specifically, I cherished a romantic impulse towards death, yet at the same time I required a strictly classical body as its vehicle; a peculiar sense of destiny made me believe that the reason why my romantic impulses toward death remained unfulfilled in reality was the immensely simple fact that I lacked the necessary physical qualification. Specifically, the pleasure of the act or fantasy of destroying a body required that the body be classically perfect and beautiful."[27]

For decades, fantasy sufficed to meet Mishima's needs, but finally, suffering the infirmities of age and great dissatisfaction with his literary career, Mishima built his body to perfection before committing hara-kiri in real life.

One of the most detailed fantasies I've ever read came to me anonymously through the *CELEBRATE The Self* request for submissions. If you're squeamish about such things, you might want to skip this one.

> One night I'm at my fiancee's house and
> we're kissing and petting on the sofa, and drinking

wine. Suddenly I become dizzy, and then I faint. I regain consciousness in the back seat of a car, my girl's father on one side of me, her brother on the other. The woman, Lydia, is driving. After stopping in front of an old shack deep in the woods, the men drag me from the car into the shack, strip me naked and throw me on my back across a table. My ankles are fastened to the front two legs of the table and my wrists to the back ones. My head hangs over one end of the table, my balls over the other.

Lydia tells me gently that I need not be afraid. She is fond of me, and is sorry that she must cause my death. It is the only way she can reach orgasm. But she promises that she will make these remaining minutes very pleasurable for me.

I watch her as she undresses. She is beautiful and has large breasts, full and with erect nipples. Her waist is thin. Her belly bulges seductively below the navel. The old man keeps his clothes on, but the young man also strips. He has a large penis already erect. He will enjoy watching me die. It will make him have an orgasm.

Lydia begins to caress my whole body, from my throat, over my chest and ribs, to my stomach. She spends a long time kissing my lower abdomen, the pubic hair and the inside of my legs. She licks behind my balls with her tongue, and gets me so hot that I get a very strong hard-on.

She begins massaging my cock very slowly and lightly. At the same time she says, "We are going to cut your balls off, and let you bleed. Don't think about it. Think only of what I am doing to you and how good it feels. That way, you won't suffer the pain and you won't even mind the sacrifice you make for my pleasure."

Lydia's brother has a long, sharp knife in his hand. The girl tells the older man to come behind me and lift my head so that I can see what is going to happen. He does, resting my head against his belly as though it were a pillow. Gently he caresses my neck and face. I can see my own genitals.

With one hand the girl continues to massage my cock. She has not released it since it got hard. With the other hand she lifts my balls upward, grasping them firmly, pulling the skin tight.

The young man comes over and crouches between my legs, which, being chained to the table legs, are forced wide apart. One hand slips between Lydia's legs. The other holds a knife. Lydia's eyes close. The tension mounts. She moans. "Now," she whispers, staring at the nuts trapped in her hand.

Suddenly I feel the sharp, hot pain as the blade slices into the pouch. Again the pain, and again as he slowly cuts through my sac. I stare, fascinated. So do the others. We are all sharing in this monumental moment. I feel the warm blood rushing down my legs, and when the man rises, I see the blood splattered over his chest and stomach and erect cock. He has a gigantic erection—cutting my balls off has really turned him on.

Lydia begins to suck my penis, and in a little while she has me on the verge of orgasm. She keeps me that way for several minutes while her brother plays with her tits and pussy. Then she says, "I am going to tell him to cut your penis, so that it will bleed freely."

Again the young man comes forward. She is still massaging my organ very gently on the shaft, but her hand is not near the glans. The man rests the blade in the opening of my cock. For several minutes the blade just rests there. We all stare at it, waiting. The anticipation is unbearable. Then he begins an easy, soft sawing motion, but the blade is so sharp that it quickly cuts, slicing the entire glans in half. Blood gushes out.

The man then comes to my side, facing my feet. Lydia bends over, all the while sucking me. Her brother inserts his huge blood-spattered penis into her vagina. They are both covered now with my blood. The woman is sucking, sucking, the blood streaming from her mouth. They are moving back and forth.

All three of them reach orgasm simultaneously, and the fantasy ends as the victim is dispatched.

Reik tells about a young woman's fantasy of going to a butcher shop after closing hours and announcing, "Please, I would like to be butchered." As though this were a frequent request, he lets her in. She undresses and lies down naked on one of the butcher's stalls. She has to lie there and wait a long time, which builds sexual tension. Occasionally an employee of the butcher comes by and touches her body, testing her flesh like an expert testing an animal to be slaughtered. When the butcher returns, he also tests her body, pawing her about as if she were a dead calf. Finally, he lifts the butcher knife, but before he makes a cut, he puts his finger into her vagina. At this moment she has an orgasm.[28]

Note that in neither this nor the preceding fantasy is there a lengthy description of pain. Everyone's concentration is on the star of the show, the victim, and more specifically the genitals of the victim.

Why Masochism?

Psychoanalysts and such have offered almost as many reasons for the masochistic compulsion as there are masochists. Freud declared that all acts of masochism represented an unconscious, resexualized wish to be beaten by the father,[29] and Novick and Novick suggested that punishment might induce love and affection.[30]

Karl Menninger said that masochism, especially self-mutilation, is a compromise to avert suicide.[31]

In the book *The Misfits: A Study of Sexual Outsiders*, Colin Wilson argues that the key to *all* sexual aberrations is that, "They are all an attempt to achieve a higher level of vitality. It is as if men felt like an underpowered electric light bulb that scarcely gives off enough light to read by; but then, in certain moments, the bulb blazes with a radiance that lights the darkest corners of the room."[32]

Wilson says, in effect, that all of us are basically bored

with sex, that sadism and masochism are some of the games we play to make sex more interesting.

Wayne Schumaker, in his book *Literature and the Irrational*, reaches a similar conclusion: "Only some such view of the relationship of suffering to well-being can account adequately for the widespread practice among primitive races of self-torture, which is by no means limited to experiences of grief. 'Orgiastic self-tortures,' says Yrjo Hirn, 'may be adduced as the most remarkable proofs of this desire for an enhanced sense of life which lies at the bottom of all our appetence;' and the remark, although pre-Freudian, has cogency. What more swiftly than pain can convince us that we exist, that there is blood in our veins and flesh on our bones, that the life which may have begun to seem dull and uninteresting is still precious? One satisfaction produced in spectators of tragedy is thus not wholly different from that obtained by lying in a position which increases the pain from a sore muscle. The effect of both vicarious and physical pain is an enhanced feeling of our own vital reality."[33]

Such attempts to explain masochism are insightful, but don't speak to *ultimate* causes. What's more, there may not *be* a *single* cause, any more than there's a single cause for shyness or trick knees. Here are some reasons that masochistic fantasies might be critically important to the sex lives of millions of people:

Sadistic Role Reversal

Conscience can really do a number on the sex lives of most people. We've already discussed the fantasy of a man who brutalizes an innocent victim by tearing the testicles off with his teeth while forcing the victim to fellate his monstrous penis. Obviously this is a sadistic fantasy, since the spotlight never shifts from the attacker. But what about the man who is captured by a gang, raped repeatedly, then choked to death while the murderers bask in his beauty? What about Yukio Mishima, who wants to destroy perfect beauty? A strong sense of right and wrong would prevent him from actually killing a beautiful young man for the sensation of destroying him. But nothing kept Mishima from destroying his own perfect beauty with a clear conscience.

Most of us are not so driven to perform sadistic acts that we're tempted to go beyond fantasy. Usually, fantasy is more than satisfying, but some people have such strong consciences that even in fantasy they can't harm another. Instead, they choose to harm themselves, actually becoming the victim of their own punishments. They are *truly* identifying with the victim—otherwise their consciences would be troubled and the fantasy would be ineffective. But they are also identifying with the sadistic aspects of their nature.

To understand what is actually generating the lust and making the fantasy work, the fantasizer has to understand, for example, whether he is looking into the face of a man being strangled or into the eyes of a lust murderer. He is the cameraman; where is the camera pointing? Once he understands the truth, the fantasy might lose its power to arouse. On the other hand, it might open the door to more potent fantasy.

Atonement for Guilt

There's an obvious link between sexual guilt and shame on the one hand and the need to do penance before enjoying orgasm on the other. It's true, in the history of human civilization: "Without the shedding of blood there is no remission of sin." Often the blood being shed did not belong to the sinner. Among the Mayan and the Aztec, it was the blood of a human enemy. Among the Hebrews, it started out that way, apparently, and then became the blood of a lamb or a bird. In Christianity, it became the blood of Jesus. Sexual guilt and shame may lead to *sadism*, in which, in reality or fantasy, the sadist abuses an innocent and pure victim in order to release his own sexual pleasure.

Sometimes, however, the victim abuses himself.

The following "confession" permits little argument:

"I'm a 16-year-old boy in a 19th century seminary in Europe. I'm caught naked and masturbating in my cell, and am dragged before all the other boys. Two priests order me to lie on the table naked, which I do. The other boys surround me closely. I am ordered to show the boys the sin that I have committed while one priest goes to my head and lifts his robe, draping it over my head. The other priest steps between my legs, placing his robe so that it fits tightly under my testicles. None of the boys knows exactly what the priests are doing. Only I know.

"Quickly I get an erection. My hips gyrate with pleasure. I try to resist coming, but the priests insist. The boys surrounding me are pulling on their penises, too, and suddenly they have daggers in their hands. At the moment I arch up off the table in an explosive orgasm, they plunge the blades into me."

The man identifies as a pure, innocent, blond-haired, blue-eyed seminarian who becomes the savior of the seminary world. For the sin of his own orgasm and that of the priests and other boys, he is slain, thereby cleansing them all of sexual evil.

The function of at least one type of masochistic sex fantasy is to assuage guilt. Says Theodor Reik, "The need for satisfaction of the guilt-feeling explains the necessity for the suffering...[34]

Reik continues, "Therefore the masochistic scene or phantasy falls into two parts which must be sharply discriminated psychologically and which only in the end-phase grow into a unity. First discomfort, humiliation, punishment: then pleasure and instinctual gratification. To put it theologically: first the atonement, then the sin. The discomfort is not desired as such, but it constitutes the price of pleasure. Finally the pleasure edges into discomfort itself. The atonement itself is transformed into a sin. The flagellation which originally served the purpose of self-castigation with early Christian monks and ascetics later became a means of sexual excitement. The increase of pain produced ecstasies. Ultimately the Church was forced to forbid too severe expiatory practices because they frequently led to sexual gratification."[35]

Many examples of masochistic fantasy are no more complex than this. It's an attempt to atone for the anticipated pleasure. For those who have been raised in the sex-negative environment of some religions, the punishment may be brutal—mutilation and death. The actual flagellants may have had the same motive—and outcome.

Narcissistic Power

But for other masochists, it's a different story. And even the orgasmic outcome may be completely different. The masochistic fantasy invests the sufferer with all the narcissistic attention and power. Says Reik, "The description of the masochistic character as weak, dependent, easily influenced, helpless, continues to amaze us. All these features serve the purpose of concealing the utmost determination and stubbornness. What the masochist has to say to the existent ruling forces sounds like slavish submissiveness. It is, however, a scornful 'no' to the world of appearances that became dominant. He submits—in order never to yield."[36]

In essence, the masochist in this fantasy says, "You beat me to distract me from my sexuality. You blind me, you threaten my life, you humiliate me, but watch—my orgasm will still triumph, and my sexuality and beauty will mesmerize you."

Biochemical Highs

There are two other likely explanations. First is a simple biochemical one. I have a good friend named Lloyd who jogs past my house every now and again. He's a marathon runner, and keeps in shape covering ten miles or more perhaps twice a week. I see him toward the end of his run, and I've told him a couple of times, "Lloyd, you look like hell. Why on earth are you doing it if it's that unpleasant?"

If you've ever seen such a face, you know what I mean. His jaw is practically dragging on the ground. His eyes are glazed over, lifeless. Everything about him is sagging and exhausted. And Lloyd replies, "I feel great, Harold. I'm on this high—it's impossible to describe."

Endorphins are pouring into his blood stream. Some people have called them nature's natural morphine. It isn't like a pep pill, an amphetamine. It's not like the drug Ecstasy. It's a feeling of warmth, of security, of pleasure. It's gently erotic. That's what T. E. Lawrence of Arabia meant in *Seven Pillars of Wisdom* when he described being beaten because he refused a homosexual proposition. It's what launched the self-flagellating saints on their path to ecstasy and orgasm. There is a direct biochemical relationship between the stress of the body and erotic response. Physical abuse pours into the blood heavy doses of endorphins, adrenalin, testosterone, estrogen, and many other natural psychoactive hormones.

Loss of Self

The intensity of the sexual experience is limited— sometimes stifled completely—by rational thinking. Our conscious selves and our desire to dissolve into erotic pleasure are always at war. The sole mission of the rational mind is to maintain the individual's survival. For that, it must be entirely in control. Even sleep, although necessary, interferes with the vigilance that's the reason-for-being of the rational mind.

But those multiple millions who have experienced it know that the most miraculous and transcending sex is that in which there is no self-consciousness. The French have the right term for orgasm—"the little death." Walter Braun, M.D., quotes a woman who comes quite close to explaining it: "You know, there's one thing about that night I shall never forget. At one moment the four of us were in a real frenzy—ecstasy I suppose you could call it—and at that moment I was able to forget my own personality completely... That was a wonderful feeling and I shall always remember it. It was nice for a few minutes not to be able to recall what and who I was... It was glorious to feel, for a short time, my own personality recede completely and fade away..."[37]

Perhaps among all the wonderful buttons that the masochistic fantasy presses, one is to surrender into the oblivion of orgasm, and one path to that oblivion is utter surrender to the will of others, and to fate.

CHAPTER V

Sex as a Spectator Sport

Being caught naked in public, back when it was known as indecent exposure, was the most common sex crime in America. Then some thoughtful people put together a Model Penal Code, and most states adopted it. With regard to public nudity, the theory seemed to be that the body, when not engaged in sex, and made by God in His image, can hardly be indecent. (By that same logic, the body *aroused in lust*, equally created by God, can hardly be considered indecent—but that's another argument.) Unless you are nude with the intent of embarrassing, insulting, or outraging another person's sensibilities, public nakedness is no longer considered indecent exposure in most, although not all, states. It's usually not a sex crime these days.

Instead, it's now disorderly conduct, disturbing the peace, or creating a disturbance.

The war against the nude body is an almost invisible blip on the radar screen of history, not more than half a century old at its most stringent, and existing today in only a handful of nations. The prophets of Israel wandered naked for years preaching their messages of doom. David danced naked in celebration before the throngs of Israel. Greek athletes performed naked and their warriors sometimes fought naked. Public nakedness was common in Rome. St. Francis wandered through the fields naked. Jesus was baptized naked. Before Y.M.C.A.s became coeducational, men and boys swam nude in their pools. Urinals in bars and taverns were nothing but long troughs.

One result: the apostles of body shame have created a Frankenstein. By creating a taboo of the genitals, they have elevated them to a level of preposterous importance. We say body; they think phallus/vagina/breasts.

For the past 30 years, I have been clothed, on average, no more than two hours in every 24. Sometimes I am dressed an entire day; at other times I'm not dressed at all for weeks. There aren't too many people who can make that claim in our society. I'm both lucky and grateful that I'm self-employed, and that I work with people who are comfortable being nude or not offended when I am.

So I know what I'm talking about when I say that, if one can divorce one's thinking from societal conditioning, and put aside all the negative baggage, one can feel perfectly natural and unself-conscious being nude—in fact unaware of nakedness. Then, one becomes uncomfortable with and conscious of being *dressed* when necessary. Being *clothed* in balmy weather is the condition that needs explaining, not being *nude*.

Although there may be a few out there, I have never met a person—male or female—with whom I've discussed nudism who hasn't said either, "Yes, I've been nude around others who were also nude in a social situation," or, "I like to be nude sometimes when I'm alone, or just with my boyfriend/girlfriend/husband/wife, but I'm too embarrassed to be nude around others." Excluding those who were conditioned as children to be body-negative, the people to whom I've spoken about being nude, especially in the outdoors, have described the experience as exhilarating, a feeling of freedom, awesome, a real high, and such.

Why? Simply because it's our natural state.

In the beginning, when people find freedom in nakedness, they discover the experience is highly erotic. Here are two examples from *CELEBRATE The Self*:

The Erotic Yard

One day before work (I work second shift), I mowed the lawn. I was wearing only a T-shirt, shorts (no underwear this time), and jogging shoes. In the course of working, I took the shirt off to feel cooler. I have a decent sized yard (one and a half hours to mow) with four-to-five-foot-high hedges all around. But I live in a residential neighborhood. There are houses on the front and sides and an open alley across the back. I'm visible no matter where I am.

When finished, I put the tools away and sat on the steps of the back porch. The back porch is on the side of the house and the neighbor's side windows all have a view, plus that of the back alley. As I sat on the top step, only the porch post and half-lattice railing were between me and the house next door (about 15 feet to my side).

Being nearly naked in the warm sun had me really horny. I sat, spread my legs, and watched as my hairy nuts popped out. I started teasing myself in steps. What a turn-on to see my genitals exposed to the sunlight. I closed my legs and adjusted myself so that when I opened my legs again, my whole sack was exposed.

Next, I slipped my shoes off (a guy's bare feet are another big turn-on.) I leaned back to look at myself as I stretched out—almost bare-assed save for that small amount of cloth around my middle. I kept telling myself not to do this; if I'm seen I'll be ruined—possibly arrested. Each admonition only spurred me on.

I decided to open my shorts and then to slip them down just a bit and expose my butt and hips. That sight did it—no turning back now! I have a nice bush and light to moderate spread of dark hair on my legs, and seeing this open to the sun and touching my exposed skin really raised my fever.

Step by step I slowly pushed my shorts down my thighs and concentrated on the increasing exposure of my legs and crotch before my eyes. Finally, they slid to my feet and I took them off.

Here it is, a bright, sunny day in a residential neighborhood, people all around, and I'm totally naked now, exposed, can't hide. I pretend that if I don't look around no one will see me (all the while knowing that I'm quite visible).

The feelings of lust are indescribable as I watch the head of my (plump) dick and start swabbing it with saliva. I'm usually only half hard at this point. My dick is shiny with spit—what a sight in the daylight.

The jerk-off is slow and dedicated—all the while I'm telling myself to look at how completely naked I am, no protection now. As the orgasm builds, the final warning to myself is, "Don't stand up!" If I do that I'll be totally vulnerable—viewable also from the street in front. That's the trigger. I start to stand. By this time I can't think straight and don't care.

Suddenly I feel invincible—fuck you, world! I blow my load for all to see and somehow, unrealistically, I'm invisible. My genitals are functioning in broad daylight—right in front of them—and they don't have the awareness to look around and see. I feel so sinful and bold, and yet so satisfied. There's my semen— splattered on the walk. I've done it!   —John L., PA

This was by far the most popular letter in that issue. Many readers wrote saying that they understood exactly what John L. was talking about, especially when he wrote, "Fuck you, world!" Millions of people feel sexually repressed in our "free" society—including those who support the suppressing. Unfortunately, so passionate a protest when one is actually acting out rather than fantasizing can lead to a jail sentence. I know from experience, however, that John may very well have been viewed by a neighbor or two. Most people are not as prudish as they are thought to be. Many—perhaps most—enjoy watching.

Only days after John's letter was published, we received another:

Naked in the Night

"In your May/June issue, John L. wrote a letter about jacking off in his back yard. That was a hot story.

"So last night I was sitting out in my yard, surrounded by neighboring houses. I had about three large glasses of wine. It was dark, about 10:00 p.m. I was feeling good and horny. Then I started thinking about this letter John wrote.

"Bam! My dick was hard. I just had a pair of old jeans on over my boxers, no shirt and barefoot. I spent a few minutes talking myself into doing this.

"While sitting on the back porch stairs, I slipped off my jeans. It was nice and cool outside, and my heart was pounding. I took my boxers and pulled them off. Then I sat there for a few minutes. I lit a cigarette and got up. I walked down the gangway with my half hard dick slapping against my left thigh. I stood there smoking the cigarette, and scratching my balls bathed in the glare of the street light. *Boy!* It felt great standing there naked with a throbbing boner.

"I finished my cigarette and flicked it away, then went and sat on the stairs. I laid back and spread my legs. With a little spit in my hand, I sat there with my buddy in hand stroking and stroking. I felt my come building, so I stood up just in time to shoot it into the night air.

"I sat down, finished my wine, had another cigarette. That *felt so great.* I really enjoyed my nude body outdoors. I know it's not the biggest adventure, but for me and maybe John in PA it's enough."

Of course acts such as these are illegal in most jurisdictions—although there is nothing in Judeo-Christian tradition or the Bible on which to base such legislation. There is no commandment, for example, declaring, "Thou shalt not go naked in public." Jesus did not preach against nudity, and even St. Paul, for all his sexual negativism, did not rail against nakedness. Nonetheless, as Richard A. Posner and Katharine B. Silbaugh write in *A Guide to America's Sex Laws*, "Public nudity is a misdemeanor for first-time offenders in almost every state." Those states which have followed the Model Penal Code "require that the exposure be for the purpose of arousing or gratifying the offender's sexual desire. This provision seeks to separate nude sunbathing and prank activity such as streaking from acts of sexual aggression, prohibiting only the latter. Many states have adopted this aspect of the Model Penal Code, leaving the question of nude sunbathing to local ordinances that prohibit disorderly conduct."[1] That means, for example, that mowing your lawn nude in Denver, Colorado, is not against the law!

A few decades ago, communities all across America had their skinny dipping mud holes, lakes and beaches where people discreetly swam nude. In many of those communities today, prudes have passed laws requiring bathing suits, but fierce legal battles have been launched by proponents of clothes-optional facilities. They've argued that these places are exempt from the law because they existed before the law—and that the law has no right interfering with the harmless pleasure of others in the first place. These arguments have won judicial blessing in many cases. In others, energetic opposition has prevented laws against discreet, non-erotic nudity from ever being passed.

To make things more complicated, in some states the female breast is *not* considered a genital organ and may be freely exposed. In others, it has been specifically ruled indecent, a perspective that seems irrational beyond comprehension.

The desire to display the genitals might well be a natural instinct, part of the courting ritual, as it is in other animals. As with all instincts, it must be sated—even if only in fantasy:

Through The Looking Glass
by Don Todd

When I was a student at Washington Junior High, we all watched an educational film, a nineteenth century British sea-going saga. In one scene a bent-over midshipman was caned by his captain—and I developed an erection that persisted until I was able, in the privacy of a toilet stall, to whack it off.

Although by necessity the teenage king of bathroom quickies, my venue of choice was home sweet home, where the deliciously wicked thrill of roaming the house naked and priapic led inexorably to that narcissistic delight, my mother's full-length mirror. Before it, on center stage and watching myself perform, I became the Tennessee Williams of masturbatory fantasy.

An early favorite: Reported by "Coach" for having been caught jacking off in the shower, I am given a choice— confession, apology, and punishment before a special assembly, or a note to my parents. Although I had already been caught in the act by an amazingly unconcerned mother, I opt for martyrdom. Sparing my family the pain of learning their son was a loathsome jerk-off, I am prepared to do what a man has to do.

On stage, peering through the looking glass at my assembled classmates, I am required to describe precisely what I had done while slowly, item by item, removing all my clothing. The display becomes infinitely more prurient when, before stepping out of my underwear, it has become obvious to everyone that I am sporting a boner.

Seized, bound, I hang by my wrists, naked, helpless, as Mr. Jackson, our principal, removes his jacket, rolls up his sleeves, and then (this part is tricky) unbuckles his belt. Can there be an act more fraught with sexual implications, more likely to induce premature ejaculation, than a man unbuckling his belt? It's a wide, tooled, lethal-looking hunk of leather which he menacingly doubles. Just then a cheerleader in short skirt and tight sweater leaps onto the stage and pleads, "Give me an M."

"M," shouts the crowd. Whack! Leather explodes on naked buttocks.

"Give me an A."

"A." Whack! Setting fire to my abdomen.

Into it now, a bloodthirsty crowd is on its feet spelling M-A-S-T-U-R-B-A-T-O-R, as the searing impact of randomly aimed leather blisters naked flesh. It is a painful and humiliating reminder of an addiction I am unable to defeat.

"The buckle," demands the crowd. "Feed him the buckle."

"Give me a B," from Tight Sweater.

"B."

Whack! I begin to scream.

Unbound, body streaked with welts, I face my peers as, under avid scrutiny of Tight Sweater, I am forced to publicly masturbate.

There's certainly masochism in this fantasy, but it does-n't carry the sexual energy that the truly masochistic fantasies of the previous chapter evoke. Here, it's an excuse to bring the daydreamer naked before the students. Based on his background and his personality, he is able to *believe* the fantasy that he was caught masturbating and would be punished in front of the entire student body at the direction of a sexy cheerleader. Other exhibitionists might find it more "real" to imagine themselves a student in a sex education class, who's asked to strip and masturbate for class discussion.

In the previous chapter, I presented a fantasy by Jake, the 45-year-old substitute bus driver. He orally serviced four men, and we left that fantasy as Jake was about to get as good as he gave. Actually, the fantasy continues:

"One of the hunks is pulling down my boxer shorts, and has discovered my secret: my big, beefy cock, just shy of a full 12 inches long, and ponderously thick. My manliest possession has finally been discovered.

"The ringing silence slowly turns from a heightened hush of awe and wonder to a literal point of 'on your knees' worship as the full impact of what they are experiencing takes control of the studs. Almost as if in a dream state, they fall to their knees numbly, deliciously spread open wide my well tanned, heavily muscled thighs, and rest my heels on their shoulders. My wondrous, God-given endowments are now titillatingly exposed for all to revel in totally unobstructed.

"As if the very gates of heaven have finally been breached, a thick, invisible essence of my pure, animal transcendent musk quickly permeates the air. This, combined with the spine tingling, ball-blasting visage of my unbelievably huge cock, is erotically electrifying. Slowly, majestically the giant thing rises to well over half mast much like an anti-aircraft gun leveling in on target. Its enormous purple-pink cock head drools pearly drops of pre-cum down the shaft, copiously slathering my hefty balls. And as if in divine unison with the beat of the throbbing cock, the balls slowly rise and fall in their hairy sacks.

"Through rampant lusty visual exposure, I am now being totally and deliciously violated beyond my most lurid, wild imagining. I absolutely wallow in this unexpected erotic revelation of my most devastatingly perverse sexual beauty.

"But nothing has adequately prepared me for this overwhelming religious adulation that momentarily overcomes the horny studs. They are mute, speechless, and in awe beyond all cogitation of what they find I have had swinging in secret between my thighs for all these many years. They intuitively know that for this moment, God has inexplicably revealed himself to them through my cock.

"Clyde, the best-looking one, seems totally consumed by the fires of a feverish suck mentality. He impales his enraptured mouth on my swollen godhead right up to my balls.

As the others caress every part of my body, Clyde's deep throat sucking jolts me cosmically into that final transcendent dimension of total rapture that I have been inexorably moving toward. I scream uncontrollably, and experience an all-encompassing, all-dissolving explosion with every part of my mind, body, and soul. And for just a moment, I find myself one with God."

"In addition to experiencing the dissolution of the self which we mentioned in the last chapter ("For just a moment, I find myself one with God,"), Jake's fantasy is an unrivaled example of pure, narcissistic erotic display. His audience is utterly speechless in the presence of his sexual power—his genitals. His "endowments" start out being "God-given," and soon end up the focus of God's self-revelation, and finally the divine reincarnation as "my swollen godhead."

Although any generalities regarding sex are fraught with innumerable exceptions, it appears that women's exhibitionistic fantasies are less power-oriented, less fantastic, and more romantic. "My best fantasy," writes Alice, "is that a handsome, well-built man desires me. He doesn't have to have an enormous penis or be a real Adonis, just good looking. But what's important is that he thinks *I'm* beautiful. He's very gentle in seducing me. As I allow him to undress me, he keeps saying, 'God, you're so beautiful.' And he pets me as though he really believes he's touching something precious and special. As he touches me, his eyes seems to drink in my beauty. He can't get enough of me. He kisses my breasts and abdomen, my inner thighs, as though he's worshipping me. When he puts his tongue on my clitoris I have an orgasm."

It's certain that neither Don nor anyone else will be forced by the principal to masturbate before the high school student body. His fantasy is *functional*, not *realistic*. On the other hand, Alice is quite likely to meet a handsome man who will fall in love with her charms and beauty, and will treat her tenderly in sex.

That doesn't mean that *some* women don't enjoy more incredible fantasies. A middle-aged woman from New York City writes that she imagines herself a nude nightclub dancer: "The men actually fight to get close to me. They throw tens, twenties, even one-hundred-dollar bills. They beg me to meet them after the show. Some men pull out their dicks and jerk off while watching my tits bounce and shimmy. I lie on the floor and spread my legs, and the guys scream with desire. Now all of them have dropped their pants and are beating off. I finger myself, which drives them even wilder. We all come together."

Another woman combines sadism with exhibitionism in her fantasy. Eight men willingly sit against the wall of a long hall, their hands tied behind their backs. Halfway along the hall, a taped line stretches across the floor. Just beyond it, the most voluptuous, desirable woman imaginable (the fantasizer) sits in a recliner nude. The floor between the men and the finish line is strewn with shards of glass.

"On your mark," the woman says seductively. Eagerly, the men move onto their abdomens.

"Go!" she cries. Immediately the men begin to slide across the glass-strewn floor toward their sex object. The first one to reach her will consummate his passion. Meanwhile, the floor, speckled with blood, testifies to the woman's incredible sexual power and beauty.

But such fantasies are not very common among women. Usually the tone is gentler, more romantic, the scene more believable.

Men, too, might have romantic exhibitionistic fantasies. Here's an example:

A Music Lover

It was a hot day in the South Pacific; much hotter than usual, and working in an uninsulated, small building made it worse.

All I had on was a pair of shoes and socks and cut-off shorts. I was doing some film work in the movie booth of an outdoor theater. I was a projectionist for our battalion in the military. I had opened the fly of my shorts, so that they covered only the bare minimum of both sides of my anatomy.

I heard a knock on the open booth door, turned and saw a young, nice looking lad standing in the doorway. He, too, was dressed only in shoes and shorts. He introduced himself as a member of the battalion camped next to the one I was attached to. He commented on the "cool" attire he saw on me, and I told him I wouldn't have had that much on my body if I knew nobody would catch me while naked. He said, "Be my guest."

I dropped my shorts, and stood before him as naked as I could get.

The kid said he liked what he saw, but he was interested in the phonograph records I had. He wanted some for himself. I lent him some, asking him to return them shortly. He agreed, and said that he would see to it I was rewarded for the loan.

It wasn't a week before he said he would bring them back after the show. It was mid-week, and we'd had only one showing. After the lights had been turned off, I was alone in the booth, and preparing the film for the return shipment. I knew I was going to have company, and I knew he was not going to be surprised if he saw me naked again. So I slipped out of my clothes, and worked in comfort.

Of course it was night, and really dark. I was working with only one small light, because it was all I needed to see what I was doing with the film. Soon I heard a soft knock. I opened the door, and in walked this young man with my records. He placed them on a bench, turned to me, and without a word, shed his shorts. He stood before me as naked as I. Believe me, I took it all in, and he was gorgeous.

He said he was 18 years old, of Italian heritage. I could see his body was hairless, except for a small pubic patch. His balls were fair-sized and tight. His cock was of average size and uncut, with a tapered head. He looked at me, straight on, and said that, if I wished, *he* was my reward for the loan of the records. I couldn't believe it. How did he know? As we stood facing each other, I could see his cock start to stiffen. I got the message rather quickly. I walked over to him, put my arms around him, and thanked him. That was all we needed. Our bodies touched. The feelings that were transmitted were mutual—neither one of us needed invitations. We were very passionate in our upright love-making.

Our lips met, our mouths opened and our tongues searched. We gathered our clothes, turned out the light, stepped outside into the dark night, and locked the door.

I led him to a small knoll that evened out and contained some grassy spots. It was a favorite spot for daytime sunbathing, and some infrequent night gatherings. We dropped our clothes, shed our shoes and socks. It felt very good and sensual. So much so that each of us became more erect than expected. We came together again, and this time, each explored the other with no parts of our bodies being missed. We did not hesitate to lay ourselves down head to toe.

Each of us devoured the other. There was no hurry. Loving moments tasting the flesh with easy, smooth movement brought each of us to the final moments of pleasure. —B.L., MN

In this sort of romantic fantasy, phallically turgid nakedness—erotic display—is essential. It advertises interest in sexual activity, just as it does in real life. But the attraction results in a romantic relationship rather than objective or objectifying sex, which is much more common in male fantasies.

Voyeuristic Fantasies

Virtually every teenage boy has a fantasy of walking along the street at night and coming upon a house where the curtains are parted, a bright light is on, and a beautiful woman with big breasts (or man with a large penis) is undressing or already nude. In this fantasy, the youth hides behind a tree, pulls out his penis and masturbates. Or, the woman sees him and begs him to come in and satisfy her needs. Or, her boyfriend enters and she satisfies *his* needs. Or the poor kid is so horny he never gets beyond seeing her nude before ejaculating.

Every time we look at sexually explicit and exciting photographs or read an erotic story, we're involved in voyeuristic fantasy. It's what we do as human beings when we're not copulating: We fantasize that we observe others having sex, and, because of our rich imaginations, we convert the fantasy to reality in the theater of our imaginations and cast ourselves in the preferred roles. Voyeuristic fantasies come in all shapes and sizes, from vanilla to masochistic to sadistic and even exhibitionistic—we can pretend to see whatever we like.

But voyeuristic fantasies require for their success an awareness of the potential for participation. In other words, I might masturbate to orgasm simply watching a woman undress in her bedroom, but only if I'm also thinking, or at least feeling, "I know what her pubic hair must feel like. And between her legs, God, I know how wet she is! I want to throw her down on that bed, climb on her," etc.

The following fantasy illustrates the participatory nature of voyeuristic fantasies:

This guy and I were trapped in an elevator for about two hours before they finally got it moving again. He was really going bonkers because of the small closet space of the elevator. So we agreed he could jack off—because he assured me it would relax him, and help calm his fears.

Within a couple of seconds of our agreement, he had stripped off his shirt and tie, and was on his way to getting started. And what a treat it was to see the dude without his shirt. He was athletically beautiful, tanned, and so hot to look at that I whistled in admiration.

He grinned broadly with perfect white teeth, and was now obviously completely relaxed. "Ya like these pecs, and this big set of guns?" he said. I nodded and said, "Yeah." So he said, "Wait till ya see the rest of what this dude's got to show ya." In a flash, he unzipped his fly, peeled out of his sweaty butthuggers, and doffed his sheer briefs.

The guy then gave me a wild, bare-assed body builder's posing routine combined with a male stripper's antics that blew me away. All the while he kept asking, "How do you like this? And this? And this, good buddy?" as he struck one hunky pose after another. "Check out my groovy bubble butt, good buddy," he said. "Ain't it just begging' to be kissed?" Saying that, he laughed and gave each sweet cheek a good, hard smack.

The guy's tight cock was so sexy I couldn't keep my eyes off of it. Its thick head wobbled and shook with his every move. It was only an average size dick, but it looked so suckable, and all he-man. Swinging under that sweet cock of his, the dude had a hot pair of bull balls that took my breath away.

I told him how much I liked what he was doing and showing me.

It wasn't long before that sweet cock of his was pointing straight up at the ceiling. He kept grinding and swiveling his tight ass like he was fucking the air, and I tell you, that ass was as cute as his horny cock was. The dude had a kind of loose dance rhythm, sexy as hell, and it let him work that sleek butt and those humongous balls to the max.

Finally he began to stroke his cock with one hand, and with the other, he'd fondle and cup his showcase balls up and out to show me just how magnificent they were.

Then, swinging around away from me, and swaying loose from side to side, he bobbed that cute butt of his just inches from my face.

The luscious hair was all black and curly, and looked like it was jumping to get away from where it was. I didn't realize until then that the only hairs on the guy's body were thick clumps filling the armpits, a small, neat triangle just above his cock, and all of this wild stuff sprouting out between his butt cheeks.

My dick was jerking and jumping like crazy when the guy turned around to face me. Now his hands were all over his body, feeling and loving himself like there was no tomorrow. This dude really knew how to get his rocks off, and he was getting mine off too.

His dreamy eyes caught mine and held my gaze as he settled into a serious jack-off routine. Kind of hauling back on his haunches, he gave his body, but especially his cock, balls and titties a wild marathon workout. It wasn't too long before his breath started coming in short gasps.

A glazed look fell over his eyes, and he slurred, thick and husky, "I'm gonna cum... Oh God! Good buddy, I'm cumming!"

Gobs of his jism shot all over the cubicle like a shower. Seemed like it was everywhere. It was in my hair, eyes, mouth and even in my ears. And it just kept coming until it drooled like a string off the head of his pecker.

Finally, keep in mind that the voyeuristic fantasy can actually be an exhibitionistic fantasy in role reversal. Here's an obvious example: A man imagines someone walking down the street in the dark, passing a house with the shade up. The room is dimly lit, and, as the stranger ducks behind a tree so that he won't be discovered, he sees a naked man walking into the room. He goes to the dresser, stands in front of the mirror, presenting a profile to the window, and turns on a lamp that illuminates only his genitals. Slowly he masturbates to orgasm. Just before ejaculation, the fantasizer realizes that the stranger behind the tree is a beautiful woman.

Because the fantasy starts with the stranger ducking behind the tree, she appears to represent the voyeuristic fantasizer peering through the window. In fact, it's the man being watched who represents the fantasizer. The camera and spotlight are focused on his genitals. The voyeur would not even be in the picture if the exhibitor didn't need an audience.

Here finally, is a fantasy from a *confirmed heterosexual* who nonetheless fantasizes watching another man masturbate, then does the same as the exhibitionist becomes the voyeur. My guess is that, unconsciously, the fantasizer is playing both roles.

Beach Boners

I recently discovered a secluded cove while walking along a desolate stretch of beach in Northern California. High tide was in, so I had to climb over boulders to reach the small cove.

The remote, rocky cove had a strip of white sandy beach and lots of tide pools. I got out my camera and began taking pictures of the beautiful coastline.

Looking to the other side of the cove, I noticed a naked guy on a boulder stroking himself. He appeared to be deep in thought while he masturbated.

I couldn't help it—I stared as he stroked back and forth. Honestly, his tallywhacker was a show stopper, bigger than anything I'd ever seen in a porno movie or magazine.

Hearing my noisy camera, he looked up and was surprised to find me watching. Embarrassed, he stopped what he was doing. He tried to cover himself with one hand and reached for a towel.

I waved my arms to get his attention; I didn't want him to stop. I shook my head, "No, don't stop!"

When he stood up I could see that he was tall, lean and well built. You could tell he'd spent much time outdoors. His groin was defined by a narrow band of pale white skin that seemed to glow in contrast to his bronzed body.

He changed his mind, dropped his towel, then took out a bottle of lube from a backpack. He held the bottle over his massive boner and squirted lube all along the broad top side of his cock.

Humping his hand, he rocked his hips back and forth. Stopping suddenly, he let go and his organ sprang loose and arched upward.

With hands firmly on his hips, his bowed cock bobbed up and down under its own power, the very erect body part extending skyward from a puny patch of pubic hair.

I'm a straight (mostly solo) guy, but watching him do himself made me horny. Looking down, I could see my cock had formed a tent pole in my swim trunks. Hot, I had to cool off.

I pulled the waistband over my boner, then slipped off my shorts and ran naked into the surf. The water was cold, but refreshing.

I got out of the water and felt the cool ocean breezes blow softly over my cock and balls. I dried off and spread a towel on a boulder about 20 feet away from my j/o pal and squatted down. Stroking hard, he clenched his hand in a fist and motioned for me to masturbate too. I've done it a zillion times, but I've never j/o'd in front of a guy before.

I leaned against a boulder, my cock and balls dangling between my legs as I made myself comfortable. Then I rolled my cock between my fingers and, at the same time, massaged my pubes. I was rock hard in no time.

Looking over, I could tell my j/o buddy was ahead of me. When he tossed his head back, I knew he was about to cum. He pressed his eyes shut and his face twisted in a climax-induced contortion.

Just then his cock gushed out a torrent of white cream

that fell to the sand below. He kept pushing and pulling his penis and tugging at his balls until he was totally spent. I played with myself while I watched him cum.

His penis softened, coming to rest drooping downward beside a furred ball sac. Earlier, his brawny body resembled an Olympic athlete. Now he looked wasted.

It was my turn to perform. I squatted down into one of my favorite solo positions. I slipped a hand under my backside, between my legs, to massage my sweet spot. It's the sensitive area between ball sac and rectum.

Using both hands, I was able to stroke my cock and knead my sweet spot at the same time. I looked up to see that my j/o buddy had moved closer and was watching my antics intently.

Wanting to cum for my friend, I concentrated on what was at hand. I stared down at my cock and focused my energies on getting my fill of pleasure. I slowly pumped my fist up and down, again and again.

As I came closer, my free hand strayed up from my sweet spot to caress my pubes and pinch my nipples.

Droplets of pre-cum seeped out of my slit, giving me the lube I so desperately needed. I humped and pumped my cock and rocked my hips with abandon. When my ball sac tightened and glans flared, I knew my time had come.

My j/o partner applauded and gave me a thumbs up for my performance. He waved goodbye. I watched his soft cock swing freely between his legs as he scampered out of the cove.

—K.J., LA

CHAPTER VI

Gay For Straights

Most men and women have entertained homosexual fantasies. The imagined partner might be a close friend with whom there's an intense, even passionate but nonerotic bond. Sometimes the "love of comrades," as Whitman called it, can be so strong that it seems the only way to quiet its intensity is through sex. But that's not apt to play well with the friend—and even if it did, it could add baggage to the relationship that might destroy it. So we fantasize, and keep our erotic secret to ourselves.

Or perhaps it's a movie star that we end up taking to bed. Several happily married women have told me how much they've enjoyed Julia Roberts as their fantasy sex partner.

Leonardo DeCaprio is particularly desired among straight men because, like Chris Atkins, who starred in *The Blue Lagoon* some years back, he's androgynous—both masculine and feminine.

Here are the most common types of homosexual fantasies among straights.

Reliving the Experience

I'm speaking in generalities here—there are always exceptions: Adolescent boys have a much more demanding, compelling sex urge than do their female counterparts. (One feminist referred to it as "testosterone poisoning.") Masturbation serves to keep young lust from getting out of hand, but there is the constant drive to share one's sexuality with another. Finding the right girl is the typical ideal, but, especially early on, it doesn't happen that way. Instead, a male acquaintance, sometimes a friend, sometimes an older person, serves the need for genital admiration and erotic pleasure. This becomes the earliest shared sexual experience. As such, it has profound influence on psychosexual development. Later it provides rich fantasy material, possibly throughout a lifetime.

"The very first orgasm that I had with another human being," writes Jack W. from Boston, "I was about 14 and this man was probably in his sixties. I worked for him cleaning up this studio he had—swept it, dusted it, took out the garbage, that sort of thing. I was making a couple of dollars an hour, minimum wage. He was a nice enough guy, interested in my life, school, hobbies. He'd put out some cookies and milk and we'd talk.

"It was always on Saturdays, and one Saturday morning he asked if I'd be a model for some photos. He'd pay me twenty dollars. He said I'd have to get down to my underwear. Well, twenty dollars was a hell of a lot of money back then. I don't think my father made much more than that for a whole day of work at the factory. So I agreed. And of course finally he talked me into taking the underwear off too. I was really embarrassed, but, hey.

"Then he came up to me and took me to a full-length mirror. 'I want you to see just how beautiful you are,' he said. 'This is what I want to capture on film.' He stood behind me, one arm around my waist. A floodlight was on my body, and it was like I was glowing in the mirror. His other hand rubbed my thigh, my lower abdomen, and it felt so really, really good. I guess my cock started getting a little hard. Next thing, it was in his hand and he was rubbing it back and forth. I felt really ashamed and really hot at the same time.

"'This is beautiful, too,' he said. 'Really, really beautiful and so big.' I got so damned hot, it was like I had no will—this man owned me. His power was right there in his hand, massaging my dick. My knees got weak. He was actually helping to hold me up. When I came I blasted it all over the mirror."

The boy took the money and left, and never returned to the studio. For weeks he felt guilty, but told no one. Years later, after he outgrew the shame, he began to reflect on that incident as one of the high points of his sexual experience. Finally, he relived the experience from his now guilt-free perspective. He continues to do so, returning to a fantasy based on a true experience, and has particularly intense orgasms. Occasionally, he might even reciprocate by masturbating the man or fellating him, but only if the man forces him to do so—thereby relieving him of any responsibility for the act.

A great many boys play homosexual games during adolescence. Most look back on them with shame. Others shrug them off. Still others recall them over and over as the basis for solo sex fantasies.

What Might Have Been

More often than not, the ideal sexual experience—the one so ecstatic that we can build a lifetime of pleasure around it—never happened.

Perhaps we're actually attracted to someone of the same sex, and, for whatever reason, we aren't willing to commit a homosexual act. Maybe we feel desire for an acquaintance, even a relative, who is straight as an arrow and also married. Maybe we have religious convictions against homosexuality. Instead, we will allow ourselves to live out our desire and fulfillment in fantasies about what might have been.

Javier, from Mexico City, submitted precisely such a fantasy:

"I'm straight, but when I do fantasize for masturbation, men are the ones that appear there sucking me or being sucked, fucking me or being fucked.

"This morning I went to the gym as I usually do. I was very horny because I had gone ten days without cumming. Although I rub and stroke myself daily, I sometimes prefer to keep my seed inside.

"At the gym I did my routines, and lay over the mattress to work my ass. Bathed in sweat, I relaxed and closed my eyes. The last image I had before closing my eyes was this poster hanging there on the wall: a well defined, strong young man with his left arm over his head doing a triceps extension with a dumbbell. I rested my eyes on his nude torso and on his armpits with their golden hairs, his glance kind of lost somewhere...

"From that sight, I entered into my fantasy.

"His workout sweat streamed from his chest, from his armpits, his deep breaths turning me on. He was there to be adored like an Adonis, and to be screwed, licked, touched.

"I imagined asking him to help me with the bench press. His groin was just about six inches from my head. Deep breath, exhale, deep breath, exhale, deep...

"Meanwhile I made contractions with my pecs, while I imagined licking this guy's inner thighs.

"I helped him then, this too-straight boy. He made his moves near my jock. Was he also thinking about sex? How about him licking me smoothly, roughly? He did it. How about me licking his legs? I did it. They tasted salty. Some zones were smooth, soft, others hairy, rough, strong, steel, fed with testosterone since time began. We helped each other.

"First one, alone in front of the mirror, then the other.

"I helped him move, lifting, felt his back, his sweat. Going up and down. Deep breath, exhale.

"I was there looking at myself in the mirror, well defined muscles, strong fibers, well-built round pecs, fine tits. I saw my biceps working, full of blood, him touching them as I raised the dumbbell over my head.

"I felt the gym air moist with steam, oily bodies flushed with lust. Blind sex, everyone licking, everyone pricking, everyone touching, their clothes off, their skins tanned, their mouths busy."

The fantasy ends in a free-for-all orgy. Remember, the man is married with children and exclusively heterosexual in real life.

Homosexual fantasies are very common among heterosexual boys. That's because, unlike gay boys, straight ones don't distinguish between being heterosexual and homosexual until peer group pressure begins to influence them. (The boy who is clearly homosexual on the other hand, may realize that he has a special feeling toward men from as early as four or five years of age.) Among young adolescents, a naked body of either gender can trigger lust in most youngsters. The memory of that unrequited desire can remain pure and powerful well into adulthood, and serve as the basis of successful erotic fantasy even if the male later identifies as heterosexual:

The Coach

I am happily married. I have never had sex with a man and don't wish to. But one of my favorite sex fantasies does involve a man.

Just after turning 14, I started my freshman year at the school in my small hometown where I spent the first 18 years of my life. There were some new teachers that year. One was the science teacher, who also taught PE and was coach for girls' basketball. He was just out of college, at least six feet tall, had short brown hair, a medium to slender build, and was good with the students—but a little on the shy side.

To get to the locker and shower area off the school gym to change for PE, we had to go down a set of stairs and through a hallway on the left side of which was a room with a large glass window where the equipment was kept. Going to PE class the first day, as I walked down that hall, I saw through the window the PE teacher sitting on a bench in the middle of the equipment room changing from his teaching clothes. He was naked and just putting his foot into his jock strap. A thrill of excitement shot through me. The image is imprinted on my brain.

I'd only seen a few nude adults, and that had been older men seen briefly in the changing room at the outdoor swimming pool in the County Seat where we got to go swimming once or twice during the summer. I noticed the definition of the coach's leg muscles, his extended but soft penis laying over his balls, the brown hair around his groin and on his legs and chest, the way he seemed at ease and at one with his body, from which at that moment seemed to emanate a sensuous and erotic aura. I got the impression, as far as I was able to comprehend at that period in my life, that this man had the ability to enjoy and experience life at its fullest—including the wonderful sexual sensations that I had experienced during the prior year, when I had my first orgasm. I bonded with him then in an infatuated sort of way—I could empathize with what he as a man was capable of feeling.

Because of the less-open-about-sex mood of the late 50's and early 60's, the sheltered atmosphere in which I was raised, and the small town in which I lived and rarely had opportunity to travel from, there were no sexual outlets in a social setting for a boy my age. We lived close to the school, so I was able to go home for lunch at noon.

After eating, I used to go down to our basement under the pretext of going to the toilet, which sat against a wall at the bottom of the stairs, offering no privacy at all. I would go into the old coal bin behind the furnace. It was empty, since the furnace had been converted to fuel oil. I would drop my pants around my ankles, bend over, and imagine the PE teacher behind me rubbing his erect penis along my ass crack while I masturbated. I imagined smelling his pleasant and arousing odor, feeling the warmth and energy of this body, the hair and tense muscles of his inner thighs rubbing against my outer thighs, the thrusting of his body like I'd seen animals do, the movement of his penis sending pleasurable sensations through my anus and groin area.

At the moment I approached orgasm, I imagined that he did also, and would ejaculate with the head of his penis touching my anus. It was wonderful in that I imagined that we were both experiencing this ultimate life-affirming pleasure at the same time. In my mind, the situation carried no stigma of wrong. It was just two beings in empathy experiencing the joy of sex and life together.

It wasn't until a few years later that the guilt set in and I almost hated sex. There was no outlet and it seemed like a constant irritation, a constant call from something I could not respond to. My upbringing was that you didn't touch yourself down there, and, when you had to while going to the rest room, you washed your hands right away. Sex of any kind was off limits until marriage. I stoically held off until marriage at 31. It is just now that I've lived half a century that I'm beginning to get the simple and uncomplicated feelings about sex that I had at puberty.

My fantasies with the coach are sometimes different now, with me alternately taking the active role, but I still cherish the excitement that my image of the PE teacher generated. He was a person who liked his body and who appreciated sex, and could share without judgment or guilt, and in a loving way, the joy of it with another person.

Typically, by the time youngsters enter late adolecence, they know what sort of acts and fantasies trigger lust. Some men will turn from homosexual fantasies in shame and disgust and acknowledge only their heterosexual desires. Others, more confident in their sexuality, will acknowledge their bisexuality and happily enjoy in fantasy a consummation that never occurred in the real world.

Here's another "Might Have Been":

"Winters in Indiana can bring a snowstorm with little warning. Such was the case in the winter of 1952 when I was in my junior year of college.

"I shared an apartment with a wonderful young man by the name of Richard. Naiveté prevented me (at that time) from knowing what was really happening to me—I had fallen in love with him—but it was 1952 and we didn't admit such things even to ourselves.

"Richard, always outgoing and the life-of-the-party, had many friends not connected with our campus life. One such friend, Joe, had been in town on business and Richard and I decided to take him to dinner and a movie before he drove back to Indianapolis. All during the movie I was aware of Joe's attentions to both Rich and myself—accentuating his comments with a squeeze on the knee or a lingering pat on the leg (we sat on either side of our guest).

"We came out of the theater to find a raging snowstorm swirling around us. The drive from downtown to our apartment seemed endless as we tried to see through the white sheet of snow. Obviously, Joe was not going to be able to drive back home that night. Our apartment had one bedroom with twin-beds—how were we going to manage? There was a more uncomfortable hide-a-bed in the living room, but we didn't have sheets to fit, so we decided to take the mattress off of the sofa-bed, slide the twin beds together and place it on the top. All three of us would huddle together.

"Again, our guest was in the middle between Rich and myself. I was so excited (and a little frightened by my feelings) that I could hardly wait to get in bed with these two beautiful men—one I already knew I was feeling far too much for and the other rapidly becoming more and more desirable.

"Richard had had a very busy day and fell asleep almost immediately. I tried to appear to be asleep, choosing to lie on my side to hide my erection. Ever so gently I felt Joe's hairy body move against mine—his handsome face nuzzled against my cheek, his breath caressing my face as he gently turned my face toward his and kissed me (I had never been kissed by a man!), first gently then insistently. To my complete surprise, I responded, meeting each thrust of his tongue. I turned so I could face him and our hairy bodies joined for the first time, our erections finding a way to make their presence known.

"Suddenly, Richard awakened and told us to behave ourselves, that we should be ashamed of ourselves, insisting that he and Joe trade places in our crowded bed. Richard, who always slept on his stomach, put an arm over each of us until we all three fell asleep.

"Joe was gone by the time Richard and I awakened. It was as if he had never been there (except for the 'modified' bed under us). Before I got out of bed to dress and go on to class, Richard pulled me to him and told me that I was 'important' to him. The night was never mentioned again until many years later when Rich and I met for lunch.

"Richard transferred colleges in the spring quarter, leaving me alone in the apartment. I often would come home from work hoping that I would find Joe there, but I never saw him again. All of these years later I can still feel his arm come over me, his body against mine, his insistent kiss.

"In my fantasies over the years, Joe and I have done everything conceivable sexually. Sometimes, Richard joins us, and competes with Joe to give me pleasure. It's a wild experience, the three of us together—much more fun, I'm sure, than it would have been in reality had we gotten it on back then."

—T.H., D.C.

Anal Sex Fantasies

Some—perhaps most—straight men find the idea of being anally penetrated by another man's penis repugnant. Instinctively they identify as the impaler, the one in control, the top. Then, a curious phenomenon occurs among some heterosexual men who truly *are* in control in reality. All day long these men make decisions involving hundreds—even thousands—of employees and millions of dollars. They bark orders, hire and fire people, and wield enormous power. Such responsibilities create great stress. Some men escape the pressure through alcohol, others by sexual submission in reality or fantasy.

Just as the body strives to maintain a physical homeostasis, or balance, so does the mind. Deprived of sleep, we will sleep longer when we have the opportunity. Required to constantly be in charge, we will seek to surrender as a counter-balance when the opportunity arises.

The capacity for total surrender, the dissolution of consciousness while being impaled as an anal receptive, is captured in the novel *Boys of Life* by Paul Russell. Carlos is looking through a gay porn magazine, and comes across a picture which he explains to the narrator: "Right when the blond guy's putting it in him. See how they caught it just like that, that instant when the kid thinks, 'I'm gonna die.'... He loves that feeling of 'I'm gonna die.' See—his eyes're kinda crossed, his mouth's hanging open, you can just hear that *Ouff*! he's moaning when it sinks into him. And they've got it there, just some guy with a camera and he's catching that kind of death that's happening for this kid—this one single instant that turns him clear as some pane of glass. You're looking all the way down into him, to where he is giving something he didn't even know he had."[1]

"I've never been fucked, and I don't want to be," a man in his mid-30's, an executive at a New York publishing company, says. "It's one of those things I fantasize about, but in reality, number one I'm top dog—I don't submit to anybody. And number two, there's all those sexually transmitted diseases. But the *fantasy*—this guy just overwhelms me with his physical strength and the power of his sexual heat. He's gentle. He lays me down in the grass, caresses my body, strips me. He tells me how beautiful I am and how much he needs me, so I smile and nod and submit. In the fantasy I don't feel any pain. He lifts my legs to his shoulders, slips it in, hugs me to him. I don't have to worry about anything ever again. I don't have to make any more decisions. I'm safe in his strong arms, his hungry, adoring eyes. It's a wonderful feeling, really."

If one's daily life is one of submission, the fantasy is likely to be one of *doing* the penetration: "My boss is a fucking mean-spirited fairie. I hate his guts. I actually jerk off imagining punching him once in the breadbasket, ripping his clothes off, getting him on hands and knees with his ass in the air, and fucking the shit out of him. I make him beg for more and tell me how much he loves it."

Sometimes the act of anally penetrating can be the natural expression of male sexual aggression. A 30-year-old Dutchman reported in a recent study on actual anal intercourse, "That guy radiated something very submissive, also because he was almost half a head smaller than me. And his submissiveness induced my need to fuck him. Added to that, he kept turning on his back spreading his legs. For me, that was a clear signal that he wanted to be screwed."[2]

Whether in reality or fantasy, the psychodynamic here is apparent. Presented with the opportunity to dominate, as contrasted with everyday submission to a boss, the law, and the Church, this man's sexual aggression instantly came to the fore.

Thirty-five-year-old Manfred, another subject of the Dutch study, made the point even more emphatically: "You feel that this submissive is totally surrendering himself. Certainly, when he is tied up, he is totally defenseless. At that moment I am the one who decides what is going to happen. That gives me a great feeling. I don't let up then, because if I did, I wouldn't have any more control, and as a top, I can't let that happen."[3]

Wish Fulfillment: Affection/Love/Bonding

Freud and those following in his footsteps made a great to-do over the so-called Oedipus complex, the son's compulsion to murder the father and have sex with the mother. Now, theories are all well and good, but when a theory is presented as a universal truth affecting virtually all males, it seems that it should ring true in our conscious, everyday lives. We should be able to say, "Yes, I can see that in myself—the desire to have sex with my mother and eliminate my father from the picture."

In fact, it does *not* ring true. I lusted after my female cousins, aunts, my mother's girlfriends—and I enjoyed peeking at my mother when she was nude. But the thought of sex with her was, if anything, distasteful.

I was not *told* to feel that way. I did not suppress any attraction for her. (For better or worse, I've suppressed precious little regarding sex in my lifetime.) I simply had no Oedipal urges.

The reason I'm going on about this is that emphasis on a mythical Oedipus complex, in which sons want to kill their fathers, has blinded us to a critically important truth, one which virtually every man *does* recognize and which can shape his entire life, including his erotic fantasies: *Every man wants to love and be loved by his father*. When that affection is not forthcoming, the need can be eroticized, leading to homosexual fantasies. These are recognizable because they are more tender and loving than they are hard-core erotic. In the following example, we read between the lines that the father in actual life was a dominating, potent man. In the fantasy, the genitals have been injured, putting father and son on an even playing field where affection can dominate.

The Ohioan

He was a very nice young man, and, of course, of military age like myself. I hadn't seen him around in awhile and asked others in his Company why. I was told he was in the hospital. He had been kicked by a horse.

The story goes that he had gone for a ride on a horse that some native owned, on one of his days off from duty. For some reason, the horse gave him a good kick between the legs, and almost decapitated his cock. The kid's balls were injured, also, which incapacitated him for awhile, and required a hospital stay.

On one of my days off, I took a walk along the shore of a bay near our camp. The tide was in, which gave the bay high water, which was good for a swim. As I walked toward a convenient spot, I noticed a pile of clothing lying on the beach. I looked out into the bay and saw someone quite a ways out, doing some swimming and underwater diving. By the clothing, I knew it was someone from my outfit. I don't think he spotted me before I had shed my clothes, and started to wade and swim to where he was at.

When he spotted me, he came swimming toward me, and we met in chest-deep water. When I recognized him I called out his name.

"Clarence," I said, "how the hell are you?" He replied that he was all right and glad to be back with the outfit. I didn't hesitate to inquire about his injuries, as I believe the whole battalion knew about it. Clarence was not an outgoing lad, but seemed not to be shy about what happened and where it happened on him. I told him I was sorry about his misfortune, but he sort of laughed it off as though nothing had happened.

He told me about the accident and his stay in the hospital. He also said that the doctors had dealt with several cases like his, but the other injuries were caused by battle.

At that point, I felt brave enough to ask him if he had visited the local whorehouses as yet. He did not shy away from the question, but looked me straight in the eye and said he had never had a fuck yet. I asked him how he knew his injuries had not left him sexless. He said he had tried it out in the hospital, and the medics gave him a clean bill of health, but not to be too habitual about his sexual adventures. At that point he invited me to see for myself.

I didn't need a second invite, and sank beneath the water. What I saw was gorgeous. He was still hairless at the pubic region. His cock was hard and about eight inches long. His foreskin hung over the end of it like a rosebud. While I was looking, he was playing, and pulled the foreskin back and forth to reveal a nice oval cockhead. As he was showing me, he was pushing his cock toward my head. At that point I came up for air. I congratulated him and said he should really enjoy what he had between his legs. I don't know if he had always been so forward, but I had always pictured him as a meek, shy sort of backwoods kid.

He said he did enjoy his equipment, but he would like to have someone to enjoy it with. He said that he knew the gals in the whorehouse would give him pleasure, but that he would rather do it himself than to pay for it. I said I would like to see him do it to himself so I could see how healed he had become.

He was agreeable to that, but wanted to swim around a bit first. So we swam and dove under water and just wrestled around. During that time my cock became hard, too, and I knew that he knew it. It was during the body contact that our cocks would touch and I could feel his hands take a quick feel—accidentally. That kind of action and behavior gave me an indication he wanted and needed male companionship. I did oblige by giving him a couple of feels, too.

When we were taking a breath of air, we stood very close to each other. In fact, so close that our cocks touched. He did not pull away, nor did I. In that instant, I felt that we could be partners in pleasure. I reached down, put my arms around his waist and pulled his body as close to mine as it could get. Our hard cocks were pressed together, and against our bellies. We looked each other in the eye, as his arms went around my shoulders and pulled our faces together. Our lips met and parted. Nothing had to be said. Our tongues searched and probed and tasted.

Being out in the open water was not a good situation. The closeness of our bodies was too revealing. Very casually and softly, I suggested that anything we did was to be done under water or up on land behind the trees and bushes. He said that he thought it was a good idea. With that, he slowly sank down into the water and with one of his hands pushed my foreskin back and wrapped his lips around the head of my cock.

I did not expect that sort of thing at all. To say it felt good is not the right description. It was marvelous. It didn't last long enough. He had to come up for air.

We headed for shore, still hard. We gathered our clothes and went into the bushes. Once there, we proceeded to make love with great passion. Each wanted the other's flesh. We knew what to do, and did it.

Afterward, we lay together for a long time, not letting go. We had given ourselves to each other and had tasted of each other and it was time to part. We did not want to do so, but we did.

Most erotic fantasies end as soon as they accomplish their purpose of producing orgasm. The fact that this one continues through to a wistful parting suggests that it has as much to do with a relationship as sex.

In a similar vein, a respondent writes of a recurrent fantasy about having a fishing buddy join him in the simultaneous joys of fishing and sex along a stream bank. In the daydream, he is a student at the university's biology department, where his professor introduces him to a graduate student named Ken.

"Ken had straight blond hair, blue eyes, wore a pair of tightly-fitting, faded jeans and a similarly tight white T-shirt, both of which exhibited a beautiful torso.

"The professor said that Ken had inquired about other grad students that might guide him to the best fishing holes in the area. Knowing of my intense commitment to sport fishing, he suggested that Ken and I pair up in the fishing game. The professor then excused himself and left Ken and me alone. We shook hands, perhaps longer than normal, and smiled at one another rather enthusiastically. We instantly recognized a potentially budding intimacy.

"I told Ken that I was just about ready to leave to try out a new stream nearby and invited him to join me. He begged off, saying that he had just arrived in town and had to find a place to bed down. He asked if I knew of any inexpensive rooming houses near the campus.

"'If you don't mind doubling up with me in a big bed,' I responded, 'I'll be happy to have you share expenses at my place.' I described the small house that I recently rented on a farm just outside of town. Ken reacted positively, and we decided to drive out so I could show him the place.

"Upon arriving, I quickly showed him around (especially pausing in the bedroom), and then suggested that we walk down to a nearby stream that I often fished.

"It was a hot day, so I suggested that we take a dip. We both took off our clothes and, after viewing Ken's beautifully sculpted body and magnificent dick and balls, my prick began to stiffen. Ken looked me over slowly and carefully, smiled and seemed very pleased. We jumped into a small pool together, began splashing one another and playing tag. I grabbed Ken from behind, pressed my hard cock against his buns, and reached around his waist to grab his dick, which I slowly stroked. Ken relaxed, pressed his head against my shoulder and moaned delightfully. I kissed him on the back of his neck.

"After releasing him, we climbed out of the stream. Both our cocks were rock hard. Ken laughed and pulled my body against his. Our dicks were throbbing against our stomachs as we kissed, laughed, and kissed deeply again and again. Dropping to my knees, I stretched Ken out on the grassy bank. Instinctively, we got into the sixty-nine position and had a truly erotic suck-off, each of us rubbing butt, moaning and moving around to take full advantage of our stiff cocks and swinging balls.

Ken agreed to stay with me, and we had a glorious two years together fishing, fucking and sucking."

Phallus Fascination

Yet another reason straight men have gay fantasies is that all men are fascinated with the phallus and its functions. In 1984, David Lester published an article in *Psychological Reports* describing a study of straight pornographic films. He concluded: "The content of [heterosexual] pornographic films emphasizes close-up views of penises. Fellatio is prominent. All ejaculations are shown and the semen is visible... Aside from the few views of the female face and breasts, the content is very similar to that of homosexual films, in which fellatio and intercourse also comprise most of the film."[4]

John Holmes did not become the best known straight porn star of our time because of his body build. His stomach protruded farther than his chest. It wasn't his stage presence—his performance was awesome in its poverty. The man had one asset, a huge phallus, and straight men didn't buy those straight videos so that they could watch them with their wives and girl-friends and feel inferior by comparison. They paid good money for those videos because male genitals turn on these straight men, and big genitals turn them on big time. Big phalluses, preferably ejaculating semen, are the stock in trade of the straight porn industry.

I'll never understand why that's so difficult for some men to admit. We all take a peek at the guy next to us at the urinal. One of the best features about a locker room is that you get to look at other guys nude. What in an ideal world might be curiosity, even fascination tinged with eroticism regarding other men's genitals, becomes something else in our society. We're ashamed to own up to how we feel, and an innocent fascination gets blown into what we foolishly believe is a lurid sexual aberration: "I'm looking, so I must be lusting, and if I'm lusting after a man I must be queer."

The healthy heterosexual recognizes his interest in male genitalia as natural and universal. He has sufficient confidence in his heterosexual compulsion not to be threatened, and sufficient self-esteem to explore his interest in male genitalia through fantasy.

"A few years ago," a Minneapolis man says, "I played a game with myself that I called Fantasy Cock. A simple enough premise: If you could design the ideal penis—or male genitals—what would it look like? I would design it in my imagination, study it in detail, and masturbate in the presence of this masterpiece of male sexuality."

His Fantasy Cock was eight inches long, with a circumference of about five inches. Erect, "it would rise in awesome majesty, running wet all over with a copious flow of glans-cum," or Cowper's pre-ejaculatory fluid.

It would also "gracefully curve inward with the tip just touching my belly at the navel!"

He concludes, "As I stare in admiration at its regal form and at the growing pool of glans-cum on the floor, this wonder-cock would begin throbbing in time with my pounding pulse and in five or ten minutes, even if I don't touch it, it would succumb to its own throbbing and shoot a gigantic ejaculation all over my belly!"

Here again we have a heterosexual man who finds that, by concentrating on the Ultimate Organ, he can arouse himself to orgasm.

Why this interest among straight men? Again, there are

no single answers. As we've said, many, many men feel the absence of a father's love and affection, and convert that need into a fantasy in which they submit to serving the sexual needs of another man—a father substitute—in order to gain affection. In other cases, the Fantasy Cock that gets some men off is actually a narcissistic idealization of their own genitals, which they worship. In many, many cases, especially among educated and open-minded people, simple curiosity might lead to having gay sex, or at least fantasizing it. And of course millions of men are naturally bisexual, but for various reasons won't actually have sex with other men. So they fantasize about it.

Women and Homosex

"Romance" fantasies like the one between the two fishing buddies, which include affection as well as orgasm, are not particularly common among men, who, it has been pointed out ad nauseum, are goal-oriented in their approach to sex. Among women, however, this is a typical fantasy. In fact, romance leading to sex is what Harlequin and Silhouette are built on. It holds true for lesbian fantasies as well:

"I don't think I'd ever have sex with another woman," writes Martha. "But I do think about it now and then. She would have to be a close friend, somebody I love being with. We would laugh a lot, and cry together. In one fantasy, I tell her that my husband is having an affair, I cry my heart out to her, and she comforts me, gives me a back rub. She lifts up my sweater, unsnaps my bra, all the while whispering, something like, 'It'll be all right, honey. I'll take care of you. You know how I feel about you.'

"I feel her hands brushing the sides of my breasts, and I don't move. She kisses the back of my neck. It seems so natural. I turn around and kiss her on the lips, press my breasts against her. Well, you have the idea. Yes, a fantasy like that would turn me on—but it couldn't be just the sex."

Angela is in her late thirties, a wife and mother of two children, a boy and a girl in their late teens. She's also a college professor, and rather straight-laced. She explains, "I have had fantasies of having sex with other women (real women whom I knew) twice in my life. One was named Elise and the other Roberta. Now that I think of it, they had similar bodies—more firm than soft. Their breasts were attractive, but not large. Elise was in her twenties, Roberta in her forties. They were both outgoing and vivacious. They were androgynous. Elise worked with horses. Roberta was an executive.

"In my fantasy, I didn't feel like a woman. I took charge. I made love to them as they lie passively, delighting in my caresses. I found pleasure not in touching their bodies but in bringing them delight. My fantasies didn't include orgasms, just their bliss, their trust and happiness."

It would be easy to describe this fantasy as role reversal, a man (she did not feel like a woman) patiently caressing her, asking nothing in return. Angela adamantly insists that was not the case. She said that these two women—the only ones in her life—triggered in her the desire to control them, perhaps to dominate them. "I live my life passively in a man's world," she said. "That's true sexually as well as in every other way. We do what he wants when he wants to. When I fantasized having sex with women, I was the aggressor. Those two women are both rather aggressive, and somehow that, combined with their femininity, made me want to conquer them in bed."

"Have you ever fantasized having sex with a weak-willed man, or one who is bound with chains and ropes and at your mercy?" I asked. That scenario did nothing for her. Yet, once, at her husband's suggestion, she assumed the top position, and fantasized that she was the man while they had intercourse. Both of them had memorable orgasms, although they never repeated the scene and she never fantasized about it. She recognized the possibility that she might have identified as a man raping a woman during that scene, but couldn't say for certain.

Anecdotal evidence suggests that these female fantasies fill needs that real-life sex with men don't always provide: tenderness, romance, companionship and adoration on the one hand; the opportunity to take charge, control, and be sexually aggressive on the other.

We've been talking about the virtual universality of gay fantasies among straights—both men and women. In the next chapter, we'll push the envelope a bit. What is it like when a man actually *identifies* (in fantasy) as a woman—or a woman imagines she's a man? What does it tell us about him or her?

CHAPTER VII

Gender Benders

Some years ago, just after my first book came out, I received a letter from a sailor based in Seattle, Washington. He had read *The Joy of Solo Sex* and had an immediate sense that he could confide in me something that he had never told anyone else. He said, in effect, "I'm tall, muscular, very masculine, crew cut, even macho. No guy would cross me for fear I'd beat the hell out of him—and I would. What nobody knows is that sometimes I have this terrible urge to dress in women's clothes, even *be* a woman. I'm not gay. Only, when I get into this woman thing, I get so hot I can't stand it. Please—what can I do?"

I replied, "Once you throw out the macho male myth and settle comfortably into who you really are, I think you'll discover, like most people, that you're male and female, and all points in between. Apart from cultural influences, we are all simply sexual and, depending upon the sort and amount of hormones reaching our brains at a given time, we'll find ourselves in various preferred roles. The problem comes when we fight this natural flow of sexual expression because of societal mores or upbringing—shame or guilt.

I suggest that, in the most playful, casual way possible, you act out this "woman" thing. Siphon off the feminine tension by expressing it and accepting yourself merely as sexual, not hetero or homo—just sexual.

Several months passed and I heard nothing from "Jim." Then, one morning, this is what I found in the mail box:

> Thanks for your letter suggesting basically that I go for it in regards to my cross-dressing. I've ordered a mail order catalog from a major outfit that specializes in that. I'm still waiting for its arrival and, yes, I'm a bit nervous. I'm waiting for the extra bucks to order a wig or two also. I have three to choose from that I like. Talk about adventure!
>
> I've also called some of the gay groups out here to do a little fact finding, quite anonymously, I might add. But so far I haven't taken a head-long plunge.
>
> Shortly after your letter to go for it I tried something very daring for me. I took your advice and actually shaved my legs. What a charge! I got a screamer so hard I had to use vaseline the third time! I made notes as if I were a woman and, Harold, it blew my mind! It

opened doors to my eyes that I didn't know what to expect, but because I was honest with myself in the privacy of my own home, it happened! I wrote as if I were *really*, and I mean *really* a woman!! Even gave her a name— Jennifer! Which is—surprise, surprise—the name my mother would have given me had I been female....

I have a desire to be the female that makes love to other females. It's been "there" for as long as I can recall, it's so strong it gives me an instant throbber *every time*. And it's not that I have to be there with a dick, a dick just doesn't matter. Actually, I prefer it not to be there, especially when I'm in that mode of thinking. It's not learned,; once observed and nature (a hard-on) happens even if it's only a thought. There are times it's more my nature than anything else. Add in a lesbian sex book and I go hot. Explain that one.—Jim & Jennifer, Portland

That was my last letter from Jim—but Jennifer has written twice. She says that Jim has never been happier, that setting her free has taken an enormous burden from his shoulders. For now, he's content to keep Jennifer his private treasure, but he would like her to meet men who might love her, or at least desire her.

There are still factions in our society who would consider a man pretending to be a woman sick. Actually dressing as a woman in public is a crime in many jurisdictions. In short, a man's desire to experiment with and experience the feminine aspects of his nature are held by many to be morally repugnant, and can land him in jail.

But noncoersive human sexuality should not be a moral matter. One doesn't choose, for example, to be homosexual. The stupidest two words ever uttered by the gay community were "sexual preference" in the 1960's. Fortunately, they were quickly abandoned. I'm overwhelmed with heartbreak and anger every time I read of an adolescent who, distraught because he or she desperately desires sex with someone of the same gender, commits suicide. The object of sexual desire isn't a choice—it's *compulsion*, one which anyone with a normal sex drive cannot ignore.

But Our schools ought to teach the neurochemical origin of gender orientation. (For the record, *gender* is a *psychological* term having to do with sexual identity— masculinity and femininity. *Sex* is a *biological* term having to do with male or female. For example, a transsexual might be of the male sex and female gender.) As long ago as 1976, Robert Bahr wrote in *The Virility Factor*, that sexual orientation in males might be the result of fetal biochemistry. The presence or lack of testosterone in the male fetal brain at the critical time could either masculinize the brain, leading to normal heterosexual lust or allow the brain to remain feminized, leading to an attraction toward males.[1]

During conception each parent donates one sex chromosome. If the male donates the Y instead of the X, something very dramatic happens to the fetus. Ordinarily, it would evolve as a female. It takes a special gene, known as testis-determining factor, or TDF, to cause the fetus to deviate from its natural course and become masculinized. (In that sense, *all* men are deviates!)

Specifically, the ovaries of the fetus will begin to produce testosterone instead of estrogen, and the female genitalia will evolve into male sex organs.

The theory—and, technically, it's still theory—is that, just as external genitalia are masculinized through the fetus's male hormones from those ovaries-become-testicles, so the brain, too, is masculinized by the presence of testosterone. (The specific part of the brain that is masculinized is a portion of the hypothalamus known as the suprachiasmatic nucleus.) Here's the critical point: the degree of masculinizing depends upon when in fetal development the hormone is present—and to what extent.

We have a parallel in the physical masculinizing of the genitals. There are many cases each year of babies born with ambiguous or incompletely developed genitalia. Although babies are found to have the XY chromosomes, therefore being genetically male, they may have no external genitalia, and testicles may be found undescended, where the ovaries would be in a female. This is a rather extreme example of insufficient testosterone in the receptor cells at the critical period when the male genitals were being formed. In some cases, the underside of the penis doesn't fuse, so that the urethra is exposed. The penis may be very small, a virtual clitoris. The body's musculature may not be that of the typical male. In fact, there's a great range in what we consider the male body, although you may not be aware of it because many genetic boys, lacking substantive male genitalia at birth are castrated and penectomized and raised as girls.

There's little controversy about what causes incomplete masculinization of male babies. But there's enormous controversy concerning the hypothesis that the brain, too— which is, after all, simply another body organ—can be incompletely masculinized during fetal development. (If you'd like to learn more about this, I recommend *Sex, Cells, and Same-Sex Desire: the Biology of Sexual Preference* by John P. DeCecco, Ph.D., et. al.[2])

According to Robert Stoller, M.D., an authority on gender identity, when female animals are given male hormones, "These females shift both their normal childhood sexual behavior and their adult sexual behavior in the direction of markedly increased male behavior. Especially interesting has been the discovery of critical periods: If these sex hormones are given only during very limited periods in fetal development, the reversals in childhood and adult sexual behavior occur, but if one gives the hormones before or after the critical period, then the same aberrant behavior will not develop."

Stoller discusses the implanting of hormones directly into the animal's hypothalamus, the area of the brain involved in sexual behavior. These hormonal implants determine the animal's gender identification. In other words, female hormones create female sexual behavior and male hormones create male sexual behavior—*regardless of the animal's biological sex.*

"From these studies," writes Stoller, "emerges the very provocative thesis that in each animal there are both male and female CNS (central nervous system) subsystems for the regulation of sexual behavior.... When the normal development of the animal is distorted by the experimental use of sex hormones, the normally secondary system becomes increasingly predominant." In the natural world, the fetal brain can be programmed toward masculinity, femininity, or any points in between, depending upon the type, quantity, and timing of hormone saturation in the hypothalamus. Says Stoller, "There is much evidence that there is no such thing as an exclusively masculine or exclusively feminine mammal."[3]

In general, sexual deviation is a male phenomenon. Kinsey's scale of six degrees of sexual orientation, from exclusive heterosexuality to exclusive homosexuality, is designed to describe the entire panorama of normal male sexual orientation.

The difference between Kinsey and others of his era is that he didn't consider one stage ideal and the others inferior. All stages, in fact, are part of nature's continuum.

Harry Benjamin, M.D., writes in his pioneering work *The Transsexual Phenomenon*, "With the advancement of biological and especially of genetic studies, the concept of 'male' and 'female' has become rather uncertain. There is no longer an absolute division (dichotomy). The dominant status of the genital organs for the determination for one's sex has been shaken, at least in the world of science.

"For the simple man in the street, there are only two sexes. A person is either male or female, Adam or Eve. With more learning comes more doubt. The more sophisticated realize that every Adam contains elements of Eve, and every Eve harbors traces of Adam, physically as well as psychologically." [4]

All of which is to say in an admittedly round-about way that cross-gender fantasies aren't in the least immoral. And only rarely are they expressions of a desire to actually become a member of the opposite sex. Instead, they're just what they seem to be, a way of escaping the biological confines of one's physical sex, and exploring the truth of who we really are on the gender level.

According to research by William Masters, M.D. and Virginia Johnson, "cross-preference fantasies" are surprisingly common—the third most popular sexual daydreams among homosexual men and women, fourth most common among heterosexual men and fifth among straight women.[5]

The Woman as Man

I mentioned earlier that some women find being subordinate to men 24 hours a day oppressive—for example, working for a dominant male boss all day, submitting to a Southern Baptist husband at night. Occasionally they might need to feel the sexual power that most men take for granted. And of course there might also be a genetic factor that makes some women's sexual natures more dominant. Here's a fantasy that a close friend's wife shared with me. She's an executive secretary to an attorney, in her late twenties, tall and thin, very feminine, and likes to wear suits.

"I really don't know any women who remind me of the one I take to bed in my fantasies. She's short, delicate, very passive, with long, silky blond hair. When we stand pressing our bodies together, she has to throw her head far back to look into my eyes. I see surrender there. Her eyes tell me she'll do anything for me. I take her to bed. With strong, but gentle hands, I caress her. Slowly I remove her clothes. Her body flushes with excitement and embarrassment. I have her completely nude, although I remain dressed for a long time. I touch her just the way I would like to be touched, and I see her melt under my hands. She stretches, spreads her legs, her eyes inviting me, almost begging me. I feel utterly in control.

"I tell her to pull out my penis. Embarrassed, she nonetheless unzips the zipper. She stares at it with eyes wide with wonder. I know how she feels—she's amazed that such a large, potent sex organ is there every day hidden in my pants. I feel in myself the power a man has because of his erect sex organ, his aggressiveness.

"Still, I'm tender. I lie upon her, still clothed, while she's still so naked and vulnerable. I enter her, gently but persistently, staring into her eyes. She opens to me, totally submissive, totally mine."

Could this be an example of role reversal, in which the woman is unconsciously identifying with the submissive female? Not likely. This woman knows herself, and she really does, in her fantasies, want to be a man and dominate a woman.

Another woman has exactly the opposite fantasy. She's president of her own dress and lingerie outlet, a successful mid-sized company based in northern California. All day she gives orders to sales clerks, models, buyers. She makes quarter-million dollar purchases by telephone, drives a Porsche, has men fawning all over her—as much for her money as anything else, she's convinced. Her favorite fantasy goes to the other extreme.

She's a poor waif, selling apples on a street corner in New York City at the end of the 19th Century. She captures the eye of a gentleman from the upper crust as he's stepping out of his coach. He saunters over, buys an apple from her and turns to leave. Then he turns back. "Come with me," he says. "Don't worry, I won't hurt you."

She follows at a distance. He takes her to his town house on the upper east side. By now she's relaxed, for he has spoken kindly to her and she sees affection in his eyes. He removes her heavy clothes, leaving her in nothing but a slip. He washes her face, brushes her hair and takes her to a mirror.

"See how lovely you are?" he says. "What a pretty face! And such lovely hair!" He removes the straps of her slip from her shoulders and let them fall to her waist. "You have beautiful breasts," he whispers. "Every part of you is so special—there you were, unrecognized, standing on the corner selling apples!"

He bathes her, perfumes her, and leads her to bed. "I will buy you the finest clothes," he promises, "take you to the finest restaurants. I will care for you always, my beautiful one." And so they make love.

We rarely fantasize about the sex we are already having in real life. If we want *that*, we just *do* it— again and again. We fantasize about what, for whatever reason, we don't have and perhaps don't *want* in the real world. A woman without power assumes it in an erotic context; a woman with so much power that she is perceived as masculine fantasizes sexual submission.

Man as Woman

A young man who read about James as Jennifer in *CELE-BRATE The Self*, wrote describing himself as bisexual. He said that he'd never thought about cross-gender fantasies until the man he had sex with asked him to dress up in a woman's clothing. He did so, and both he and his partner enjoyed it. This man is a writer of erotic fiction, and so he decided to base some stories on that experience. He writes: "Then I began to get caught up in my own stories, and it was at that point that I went through a process similar to the one that you discussed; however, I used clothing to help me. Initially I would dress up and watch myself in a mirror pretending that the image was a real woman who was enticing me to have sex, but that didn't work too well until I actually became the image in the mirror and recreated the feelings and senses that she would feel and use to seduce me and the needs she was experiencing."

This man insists that he never thought of becoming a woman. He wanted to remain a man while still having the experience of a temporary but complete identification with womanhood. Unlike James/Jennifer, this man did not react to female role playing with overwhelming sexual excitement. His erotic response was that of a typical woman.

Smoke Screen Gender Benders

The following fantasy might seem more appropriate for the chapter on kinky daydreams, but you'll probably guess before you finish reading it why it's included here:

Eric, the handyman, showed up as he said he would. He was tall, young and blond, but with longish stringy hair (*not my favorite hairdo*), yet, not bad looking. He also wore loose coveralls, making any other assessment impossible. He was very positive, got right to work on the door, and told me what I already knew. The door had to come off and have the rollers replaced. He'd return on Friday with the replacement parts to work on it.

By Friday, I decided that I would have him look at my shower, too. Something is wrong with the hot water faucet—it doesn't turn the water on gradually, but all at once, letting water out full force—and then it is difficult to turn off.

Right on schedule Friday, Eric arrived as promised and got right to work on the door. He had it off its track in no time, the worn-out rollers removed, and the new ones installed.
Since he'd made short work of the door, I asked him if he had time to look at my shower faucet. He said he was slowing down for the Christmas holiday. So, following replacement of the last door parts, off he went, upstairs to the shower.

This was not the first time I'd been alone with another man in the shower, and our heading there together brought back some exciting memories. Just outside the bathroom, he asked if he could take a leak —he'd been drinking coffee all the while he was working on the door. I said that was fine, and waited politely outside, waiting to hear the toilet flush. I could hear his heavy stream as it plunged forcefully into the john, but it was quite a while following that that the toilet finally flushed. When I tapped on the door and heard his "O.K.," I opened it and went in. I could tell that something had changed in his voice, but I set about showing him the problem with the shower faucet.

He said it was not serious and that he could fix it easily, but he had to go to the truck for some plumbing tools...and off he went. While he was away I could tell he had discovered my bathroom magazines, as there was a recent issue of *Hustler* out of place on the stack.

Within minutes, he was back with his tools. He stepped into the tub, hunkered down, and set about trying to remove the handle from the faucet. It was more difficult than he'd planned, since it had not been removed ever...or at least in all the years I had owned the house. In his pulling and tapping, all of a sudden the water came pouring out of the shower-head, drenching him completely. He was able to stop the flow quickly, but not before his clothes were completely soaked!

At my suggestion, the obvious thing to do was for him to get out of those wet clothes, and get them in the dryer. He gave me a quick glance, and said that sounded like a good idea to him, too!

As he stood there in my bathroom removing first his shoes and socks, and then his coveralls and shirt, I could see that he was more muscular and well defined than I had imagined. His huge chest was covered with blond hair, and his abdomen rippled like a washboard. As he slid out of his coveralls, I could see why he wore loose ones. He needed room for that huge bulge where his genitals hung below his rippled abdomen. It surprised me that he was not wearing shorts, and he stood there before me looking for all the world like Mr. America...in the buff...and hung like a horse.

Somewhat embarrassed, I gathered up his clothes and took them downstairs to the clothes dryer, put them in and turned it on. By the time I got back up to the bathroom, Eric had again picked up the *Hustler* magazine he obviously had peeked at earlier—and there he stood, looking perfectly gorgeous with a raging hard-on. His cock and big balls were as magnificent as the rest of his body, and he obviously was not embarrassed by his unplanned nudity.

He surprised me by asking if I liked what I saw. I obviously did, as evinced by the bulge which had stretched my trousers to their limit at the crotch. With that, he put down the magazine and started unbuttoning my shirt. I melted in submission!

As he stripped me, garment by garment, our bodies touched and I could feel the growing electricity between us. Gently passing my hands over his muscular body, I quickly found his raging-hard manhood—it stood straight out an ample distance from his crotch. And his balls were huge—each a handful by itself—and swinging low in their soft, round ball sac, which much to my surprise had been recently shaved.

Since we were both now nude together and in the bathroom, I suggested we take a shower. He agreed without hesitation. Since he now knew the foibles of the faucet handles, he turned on the water carefully. Then he led me by the hand into the forceful stream. The hot water and his warm, soapy hands felt so good on my body. It had been a long time since I'd had the pleasure of showering with another man. He had no hesitation about soaping and fondling my hard cock and balls and admitted that sex with men was his secret pleasure, though everyone thought him to be very straight.

As the water began to cool, we decided we had exhausted the hot water supply, and should get out and dry off. That too, was comforting, as we gently rubbed soft terry-towels over each other's bodies. Kneeling down to dry his muscular legs, I couldn't resist his raging-hard cock pointing at me, and I gently sucked it. Both hands quickly found their way to his big balls and I delighted in manipulating them within their soft, low-slung sack. His sighs and moans told me that he was enjoying this, too. As I slid my tongue under and around his big cock-knob it stiffened and grew harder.

He lifted me back to my feet, and, as he finished drying me off, asked if we could go to the bedroom. I excitedly agreed! Again, he took me by the hand and gently pulled me down onto the bed next to him and wrapped his arms around me. I felt so warm being enveloped by his masculine strength and touching his hairy body for its full length. The projections from our crotches pressed and pulsed against each other, and our hairy chests rubbed nipple to nipple as our excitement grew. Lying close with just enough man-to-man contact, he asked with childlike curiosity if I ever did anything "kinky?"

Asking what he meant, he elaborated, mentioning vacuum pumps, cock rings and vibrators. I said that I had used all of those...and there was a quiet pause. I broke the silence with a question of my own, "Have you ever tried insertions?" "If you mean sticking something up my cock," he responded, "I've heard about it, but I thought it would hurt, so I never tried it."

I explained that I did it often, that it doesn't hurt, and that in fact, it is a very exciting sensation that few men ever experience, a sensation like no other! Eric got quiet again, and just continued our embrace, but stopped moving his hands for a few seconds. I could tell he was thinking hard! When he broke the silence, he asked if I would show him what I did with insertion. I of course agreed and broke our embrace to get the insertion equipment from the dresser drawer. He propped himself on one elbow, fascinated at what I was doing and what I was about to show him.

Following a thorough cleaning of my stainless steel insert rod and my hands, I proceeded to kneel on the bed near his head and brought the tip of the rod to my meatus (piss slit). Already thoroughly lubricated with pre-cum, I swirled the tip of the rod in it. With mild pressure, I spread my "lips" with the rod's rounded tip, and slipped it into my hard, fat cock head. Eric was fascinated and breathing a bit heavily with excitement. I could see out of the corner of my eye his cock stiffening.

After a few brief passes in and out, I pointed the rod straight up and let go of it. Eric gasped as the rod slid slowly and completely into my cock under its own weight. I could see his dick stiffen and stay very firm as he looked in amazement at the disappearing steel. He reached out and wrapped his hand around my steel-stuffed dick to feel the rod inside. Feeling his hand on my cock, I pumped more pre-cum out of my opening—right past the steel. Seeing it running down the underside of my cock, he bent forward, gently grasped my balls with his free hand, and rubbed my pre-cum all over his lips. He then engulfed my cock completely into his mouth, feeling around with his tongue for the steel inside it.

That was all it took for me! My raging-hard cock started throbbing uncontrollably as I shot wad after wad of hot cum past the steel into his mouth. I haven't experienced such intense orgasms in a long time—at least with another man.

The first hint that this is a cross-gender fantasy is Eric's masculinity: "He stood there before me looking for all the world like Mr. America...in the buff..and hung like a horse!" Eric takes the active role in stripping Jim, the fantasizer. Jim is passively lifted back to his feet by Eric, who finishes drying off and suggests they go to the bedroom. "Again, he took me by the hand and gently pulled me down onto the bed next to him and wrapped his arms around me." Then Jim asks Eric, "Have you ever tried insertion?" He might as well have said, "Have you ever fucked a woman?" Eric gasps and watches in amazement as the steel "rod" slips into Jim's urethra/vagina. Eric's rod is bathed in Jim's lubricating fluid.

It's at that moment in the fantasy that Jim passes over the brink into orgasm: "That was all it took for me! My raging-hard cock started throbbing uncontrollably as I shot wad after wad of hot cum past the steel into his mouth." But Jim wants something more from the fantasy. Although anal penetration satisfies the need for many men to play the woman in both reality and fantasy, that doesn't work for Jim. He wants his sex organ, his penis, to be penetrated by a man, and sure enough he fantasizes that solution. To do so, Eric, too, has to submit to penetration: In another fantasy, "He moans in ecstasy as I rotate and slide the rod down into his stiff cock. I lick the pre-cum from his dick-head; from around the tube [now a hollow tube rather than steel rod]. He squirms and moans in pleasure. Turning back into parallel position, I aim my fat cock-head toward his, and gently slide it onto the remaining half of the cum tube. Slowly moving toward him, I slide my cock all the way down onto the tube until our slippery cock-heads press firmly against each other.

"We lie quietly at first, sharing the thrills of our new connectedness—knowing we are now intimately joined as never before. As each cock throbs and pulses, the other feels it and responds with a throb of its own. With just these very gentle pulsing movements, we thrill each other beyond belief...until we can hold back no longer.

"With cock throbbings now steady and rhythmic, a huge load of hot cum pulses down the tube from his now giant, rock-hard cock, into mine. I slide my cock back slightly on the tube to watch his huge load of cum pumping though it. The sight of his giant pulsing cock and feeling the pressure from his cum to my cock triggers my ejaculation, and I start pumping cum, mixing it now with his, forcing both loads back into his beautiful cock. Breathing heavily, we moan with pleasure beyond belief as every throb and pulse heightens our double ecstasy."

Jim concludes that they spend the night in each other's arms "knowing we've become one as never before."

Jim uses this same basic fantasy during heterosexual phases: "A woman with an exceptionally long, large and hard clitoris inserts the organ into my cock for it's full length. Jerking off and sliding my cock back and forth on it, all the way to shared orgasm, would be a fantastic experience for us both!"

Again, Jim identifies as the woman who is being impaled by the male.

I'll talk later about sharing sexual fantasies, but obviously there are some fantasies that are best not shared with some partners. The scenario is not hard to imagine:

"Do you mind if I put your slip on? I'm pretending I'm a woman."

"That's sick! Besides, if you're a woman and we're having sex, that makes me a lesbian!"

A more reasonable approach, as described by Harry Benjamin, M.D., is to simply ask the partner to climb on top.

What occurs, according to Benjamin, is often "a mental state during intercourse in which the penis seems to lose its identity of ownership. 'The penis may just as well be my wife's being inserted into me as vice versa,' one patient expressed it. Another one said bluntly, I don't know whether I screw or am being screwed.'" [6]

Some months ago, I read that in high schools across the country, especially those in metropolitan areas, more and more young people are *identifying* as bisexual. The irony is that they are *not* bisexual, but young people these days consider it sophisticated to recognize both male and female elements in each of us, and they're laying claim to their *right* to express any aspects of their sexual natures that they choose. That attitude is a breath of fresh air. It's reflected in this insight by science writer and editor Gobind B. Lal: "Recognition of the harm done to men and women by absolute, institutionalized separation of the two varieties of human beings is not new. A minority of radical thinkers, saints, poets, lovers, and rationalists, under mighty male tyrannies of kings and priests, remained dissenting believers in the similarities of man and woman. After all, everybody knows that a boy has a mother, whose nature he inherits and acquires in various ways, and a girl has a father, whose nature she receives in all sorts of ways. That means that there is no singleness of male or female sexness in any human individual." [7]

Recognizing that fact can reduce stress, cultivate self-understanding and acceptance, and lead to some mighty pleasant orgasms in the bargain.

CHAPTER VIII

Kink

No doubt some of you have already grasped the irony of this chapter's title. What can be more kinky than fantasies of rape or strangling, or masturbating naked from a rooftop, or some of the other daydreams we've discussed? The answer is in the definition of *kink*.

Whether or not a fantasy is kinky or bizarre is subjective. It may be kinky to you, but not to your brother or your best friend. Usually we decide something is kinky because *we* haven't done it or thought about it. In that sense, a good many fantasies that we've already discussed are kinky for most readers. We tend to specialize in just a few favorite fantasies, and most of those are quite similar, almost variations on a single theme. No matter how peculiar, those fantasies which have been with us for years seem normal. It's the other guy's that are kinky.

But I'm going to use a more objective criterion for kinky. So far we've been discussing the most common erotic daydreams. Kink, for our purposes, represents fantasies that *appear* to be uncommon. I emphasize *appear* because some fantasies are simply not talked about, even in untraceable surveys. Since no one will talk about them, there's no way to know how common or uncommon they are.

At their core, even the most bizarre fantasies meet all the criteria of any effective erotic fantasy:

1. *An antidote to boredom.* Typically a boy gegins his sexual fantasy life in adolescence by conjuring up a single beautiful woman with whom he has sex. Perhaps he will change her hair color, her breast size, even her age. By the time he's 18, he's bored with her. So he brings another girl into the fantasy as well, and a year later a boy, and before he's through with that general theme he and the girls and the boy are having sex on a stage surrounded by naked men who masturbate while watching them.

Sexual boredom and the accompanying need to mate with a variety of partners may be hard-wired into the male sex drive. If so, it may have been critical in determining the survival of the species. Today, we no longer need multiple mates; yet men continue to seek out variety. And, at least in fantasy, they will do what they can to provide themselves with new experiences.

2. *The fantasy must be believable.* As we'll see in a later chapter devoted to the subject, making a fantasy believable is nothing more than autosuggestion, once known as autohypnosis. Regardless of how outrageous or unbelievable the concept

is, it's possible to suspend disbelief and accept as true the most preposterous fantasies:

"I live in the woods, miles from anywhere. Late one night, I heard the screech of tires and a huge crash. I ran out to find this young man lying on the ground, all but dead. Well, I'm a research surgeon (in my fantasy), with an operating room and laboratory in the basement. I carry him inside and prepare him for surgery, but he's bleeding everywhere. Both his arms and legs are smashed beyond recognition. In order to save his life, I remove them. His abdomen has been ripped apart, his intestines hanging out, his organs bared. I remove them all and cauterize the bleeding. I feed him intravenously.

"His face is remarkably uninjured. Yet, he's in some sort of coma—he doesn't speak and he doesn't seem to see me. Yet, his eyes are open. And he has a permanent erection."

The victim, of course, becomes a docile live-in lover who is nothing but a penis and a receptive mouth. Here you have a typical dominance fantasy, among the most popular types, with an imaginative twist to rescue it from the realm of the monotonous. And, since believability is in the mind of the imaginer, it meets that criterion, too.

3. *It involves control and power*. In this fantasy, the power is so obvious that it requires no comment.

4. *It celebrates narcissism*. I interrupted the "doctor's" fantasy before the full extent of his narcissism became clear. He penetrates the legless torso while masturbating "it," penetrates the mouth, even ejaculates into the hollow abdominal cavity. In another fantasy, he allows the beating heart to masturbate him. He uses every part of the victim to satisfy his sexual whims. The young man's entire being plays homage to his master's sexual organs.

Following are some of the less commonly reported fantasies submitted for this book. Some may be rare, even unique.

Pedophile Fantasies

I've defined kinky as those fantasies which are infrequently reported. That doesn't mean that they aren't common, but it's safer to admit in our society today that you let your dog lick your genitals than to confess to fantasizing about sex with someone under the age of 18. I don't believe I'm too far off the mark when I speculate that *every* heterosexual man with a typical sex drive has fantasized having sex with a virgin. And every gay man would have happily embraced in his fantasies a young John Travolta, Chris Atkins, or Leonardo deCaprio. But I have nothing but anecdotal evidence for that opinion, street corner conversations with buddies, personal interviews, letters, my own fantasies. No one has ever done a Kinsey-style survey and asked, "Have you ever fantasized sex with a teenager?"

I received two pedophile submissions from *CTS* readers, both anonymous:

> Most but not all of my sexual fantasies are about adolescent boys, maybe 16 years old. The sex acts would be legal in many states. In my state, however, the age of consent is 18.
>
> The fantasy: There is a new family in the neighborhood, a woman with two sons. One of the sons is restless. He is blond, wears shorts and a T-shirt, and often wears thongs on his feet. We talk a lot. One day he comes over for a visit. We are sitting on my couch. He is asking me if I am gay. Gulp! "Maybe a little bit," I tell him. He tells me that he thinks that he is gay. We talk about that. He kicks off his thongs and lays his legs across my lap. I begin to massage the calves of his legs. His bare feet attract me. I like boy

feet a lot. I massage his feet. I am getting aroused. I run my hands up his legs.

Now I am telling him I can massage his whole legs if he takes his pants off. I open the hide-a-bed where we are sitting. Now I unsnap his waist. He raises his hips and I slide his shorts down. While I am doing that he takes off his T-shirt. He is wearing boxer shorts. His erection has one leg tented up. I rub his thighs, especially the insides. I run my hands up the legs of his boxers. I reach his balls and I can feel his cock on top of my hand.

I reach to undo his boxers. He raises his hips as I slide them off of him. Now he is lying on the hide-a-bead completely naked. He is as beautiful as I imagined him to be. I am asking him if he wants me to go on. He syas, "Please! Please!" I rub his cock against the sides of my face. He wants me to take it, but I want more foreplay. I lick his precious naked balls for a while. I begin to suck his naked cock. Soon he is shooting.

Now the sex is over. We are hugging each other. He is feeling my bulge (I still have clothes on).

If that is not enough fantasy, I usually continue this way:

The boy is telling me that he has a friend who would like the same thing. A day or two later he shows up at my door with his friend. We all strip naked. I see his friend's hard cock. I can hardly wait! It is beautiful. It is pristine, naked like that. It look so luscious! The boy is nervous but eager. I get into some oral foreplay.

I don't have to go any further!

Nothing even remotely like the following has ever happened. It is purely imaginary.

I am walking down by the river. I am almost always alone there. I am surprised now to see a boy, maybe 12 years old, at the water's edge. He is wearing boxer swimming shorts, and wearing them very, very low. I am wondering if I should leave. I do not want to spoil his fun. He sees me and says, "Hi." Since he is not alarmed, I walk over to him.

"I like the way you wear your shorts," I say. "You have a nice belly."

"My cock is all that is holding them up."

I can see his bulge. "Can I feel it?" I ask. He steps over close to me and thrusts out his bare belly. I decide to reach into his shorts and feel it bare. He seems to be willing. I do that, and when I lift his cock, his shorts drop to the ground. His boy-cock is up stiff.

"I like people to see me naked," he says. "Do you like to be naked, too?"

"Yes," I say.

"Guys like you always have huge cocks," he says.

"Mine is just normal," I say. We step into a clear spot in the bushes and I strip.

"Yours is more beautiful," I say. We lie down and feel each other's cocks and balls.

He spreads his legs, throwing one leg over mine. I pull his crotch up so it is near my face. He does want me to see it all. There is no questions about that.

Now I am rubbing my face on his cock and balls. I am licking around. He does not have pubic hair yet. I lick where it soon will appear. Finally, I can't stand it! I kiss his balls at the base of his cock. I take his perfect, naked cock in my mouth. He thrusts in ecstasy. And it is done.

Now I want an orgasm. I ask him to let me lick his crotch while I jack off. He loves it! He asks me to suck him again.

Usually, that is enough. If not, I add to the fantasy by accidentally meeting him there again. This time he has a friend with him. He is telling his friend what we did, somewhat to my embarrassment. Soon all three of us are naked. I do both of the boys. This time when I jack off I tongue the friend while the first boy feels my balls.

I rarely get that far in my fantasy.

I use a lot of variation with this one. Sometimes I even fuck the boy's mother! Sometimes the mother knows about me and her son, and approves. Usually, though, the mother is not at home.

I am at the boy's house. We are watching TV. He asks if I mind if he watches in his underwear. I don't mind! Of course not! No way! He goes to his room and comes out wearing only a thin pair of briefs.

We are sitting on the floor leaning against the couch. He is watching TV. I can't take my eyes off of him. He notices that. He spreads his legs a little, posing.

The TV show ends. He invites me into his room. He wants to show me something, he says. He closes the door, then strips his briefs off.

"There," he says.

The disorder of the room appeals to me. There are a few dirty clothes lying around. It is very much a boy's room.

"Take your clothes off," he says. "Come on, let's get naked!" I cannot resist. Soon I am naked and we are lying on his (unmade) bed. This is a dream come true!

I proceed to lick his naked balls. I press my face into his crotch. I suck his naked cock. I feel his boy-load shooting into my mouth. It is all perfect. He loves it!

Sometimes, in this fantasy, I am spending the night with his mother. She is out shopping, or something during the above episode. In such cases, the fantasy sometimes proceeds as follows:

It is bed time. The mother and I go into the bedroom. She is very tired, but we have excellent sex. I cannot get my mind off her son, though. I shoot really hard thinking about him.

Now it is very late. The mother is asleep. I get up, naked, and go into the boy's room. I slide my hand under his covers and feel his crotch. I feel his cock getting hard. He throws

back the covers and pulls my face to it. Once
again, I suck him to an excellent orgasm. "Was
Mom good?" he asks.

The writer offers this insight into his fantasies: "It has
been suggested that what I imagine are things I wish had happened to me as a boy. Very possibly that is true. I always imagine myself as giving the boy ecstasy and joy. I want him happy
and excited. The boy *always* has a superb orgasm. He is always
willing and anxious for more of the experience, even when it is
a first time."

Erotic fantasies often do represent wish fulfillment, the
desire to experience in fantasy that which never happened in
real life. And that might be precisely what's happening here.
But if we follow the spotlight once again, we see that it is, if not
primarily on the man, at least equally so. If this were an idealized account of adolescent sexuality, it would begin along these
lines: "I am young again, 15 years old, and there's this gay guy
who lives in the neighborhood. He's always telling me how
good looking I am, and I see him staring at my crotch a lot, and
one day I'm really horny and curious and so I go and visit him."

That's not happening in these fantasies. Apart from
interviewing the man, it's not possible to know what's going on
in his head, but I will offer at least one possible explanation.
And I think it might apply to a significant percentage of actual
cases of pedophilia as well.

Unlike many fictional and real life accounts of
pedophilia, these fantasies have no hint of violence and power.
There is no coercion. In fact, the man and boy seem to participate in a mutual admiration society. They flatter and compli-
ment each other, and each gains enormous pleasure from the
encounter. Afterward, they hug, they chat, they joke. They are

virtually as one in their unity. And I think that's the key. The power exercised here is love, perfect love—the ultimate in narcissistic love. For it's my guess that the man—now in his late 60's according to his unsigned letter—is making love to the strikingly beautiful adolescent he once was.

In real life, he looks in the mirror and sees all the signs of aging, realizes that he cannot hold back the clock, that he can never again be young and beautiful, frolicking nude along the beach, stunning others with the potency of his erection. (Indeed, he had been a sexually precocious and attractive youngster, often swimming and sunning nude around others, although never, apparently, intimate with an adult.) Through his fantasies, he can bring that youngster to him. Together, they unite in love and bliss and orgasm, and part of him becomes young again. This isn't wishing to be a child and have sex with an adult. Nor is it an adult wishing to have sex with a child. This is an older man wishing to incorporate into himself the younger man that he was through erotic fantasy.

> Across the fields of yesterday
> There sometimes comes to me
> A little child all lost in play—
> The child I used to be.

Technically, I suppose this next fantasy would be considered pedophilic, too, for it involves an adult woman and a minor. The complexity is that the fantasizer is an adult male daydreaming about his adolescence and either a real woman doctor or one he invented for the part. A good deal of creativity is expended in the fantasy:

My Sexy Doctor and Me
> I was 15 and just beginning to jack off. I had
> a leg infection, and Mom took me to her doctor.

Dr. Levine was a big, chubby woman with large breasts. She put me on the table and took my pants off. She began to treat the sore on my thigh. As she was touching me, I got an erection in my shorts. I was embarrassed—she had to notice. I tried to put my hands over it.

She smiled and said, "It's okay, I'm a doctor. It's normal for young boys to get hard." She asked questions: "Do you masturbate?" I said yes. "Do you ejaculate?" I hesitated. "I mean, do you squirt or cum?" I nodded yes.
She took my hand away and touched my bulge.

"Let me take care of the problem. Be quiet." She pulled my shorts down, and my six inch cock was hard and up. She began to stroke it up and down. "You have a nice cock," she said. "I want you to come for me. Okay? Tell me when you feel it."

I was twisting it felt so good. No other hand had touched my cock but mine. I knew I was going to cum soon. I mumbled yes.

She stopped, lifted my legs and put a finger in my ass. It felt so funny, but good. She opened her blouse and took off her bra, bent down and began stroking my cock between her tits. I began to squirt my cum on her neck, tits and some on her chin. She kept stroking until it got soft and drained.

"Wasn't that good, John?" she asked.

"Yes, Doctor Levine," I said. She washed my balls and cock.

The next week, Dr. Levine came to my house. Mom went to the store. She had me naked and stroked and sucked my hard-on. She let me cum in her mouth.

I went to her office. She would jerk me off and make me come on her tits, mouth, even her pussy.

My father was an invalid. I saw her jerking his cock off. Then she did me in the bathroom. I even worked for her for a year and she would J/O or suck me. She loved my young cock.
—John, NJ

Although both a child and an adult are involved, this is not a pedophile (love of children) fantasy. The fantasy is the child's, who is turned on not by kids but by big-breasted women. The doctor represents an authority figure in the boy's life, and *which* authority figure is suggested twice. First, this was not just any old doctor but *Mom's* doctor. She also substitutes for Mom in sex with the boy's father: "I saw her jerking his [the father's] cock off." Being a very obliging mother substitute, the doctor also met the boy's sexual needs. Because there's a particularly strong incest taboo in our society, few men could ever consciously fantasize about sex with their mothers. In fact, as I've said, few men find the idea of sex with their mothers at all erotic. But there are certainly *some* cases in which a relationship between mother and son is infused with a high degree of sensuality, and if in adolescence that relationship is to be drawn upon for masturbatory fantasies, the mother figure will virtually always be replaced by that of a teacher, policewoman, judge, physician, or some other authority figure.

Food Fight

If, like me, you've never quite understood the popularity of food fights in movies such as *Animal House*, the following fantasy will be an eye-opener:

My buddy, Steve, was part Korean, with thick, wavy hair tight on the sides and professionally unkempt on top. His wardrobe matched his incredibly high arched eyebrows and elongated fingers. Even his trench coat fit like a glove.

For all his gothic sophistication, Steve liked to rough house. When he wasn't sharing morbid insights he was tweaking my nose and imitating Curly. Once he came to school reeking of shaving cream and claimed an overnight guest had filled his underwear with it.

"I didn't notice till I put them on this morning, and I didn't have time for another shower," he said.

But I doubted there was any such prankster, and believed Steve had let himself have it in a J/O session, as I often did.

Shaving cream was an okay substitute when food would be too messy or unavailable. But for an afternoon with the house to myself, nothing beat the total sensory thrill of a cream pie. The trick is to leave the shell intact until gravity works. Pudding has great hang time, but I found meringue too airy to be smearable.

Given my kink, you can imagine the effect our sparring sessions had on me. Birthday cake fights didn't allow the slow liberal debasement I would have liked. I got away too easy, afraid my passivity would reveal too much.

Only in my dreams did I imagine walking up to Steve and asking, "Say, I know you're a slapstick fan. How about you and I getting in an old fashioned, tit for tat food fight?"

And he'd say: "Yeah, you'd like that, wouldn't you, faggot?"

"Sounds like fun. My dad's got a video camera we can use."

"We would sit at a picnic table and Steve's sandwich would fall apart from too much ketchup, mustard, and mayo. I'd think this was hysterical, and he would silence me by shoving the whole mess flat in my stupid face.

"Okay," I'd sputter, flicking soggy bread out of my eyes. "I guess I asked for that. Satisfied?"

In my fantasy, Steve then shook up a can of whipped cream and sprayed me down like I was on fire. Calmly I reached across the table and pulled him by the hair face down into a bowl of mashed potatoes.

Holding him there, I circled around to his side. He tried to get up, so I gave him a swift kick in the ass after I packed the seat of his shorts with raw eggs. What are raw eggs doing at a picnic? It's a fantasy! I can have pancake batter if I want it. And I want it—all over me!

I haul him out of the bowl with my left hand and pick up a pie with my right. Steve sees it coming and pushes my arm up toward my own face. Splat! He twists the tin in my hand, smearing the pastry around.

I trip over my own feet and fall onto the grass. Steve puts the toe of his boot in my mouth and leans his weight on my jaw. The fact that I was helpless wasn't lost of either of us.

"Open your fly," he ordered, and quickly sat on me while I obeyed. His knees pinned my arms down and his ass was only inches from my mask of goo. How humiliating! The table was close enough for him to reach the pancake batter and I knew what he had in mind when he pulled the crotch of my briefs down. "Please, I'll do anything...."

Steve simply sat on my face and I was muffled by cracking shells and a mouth full of yolk that had soaked through. Holding the jug as high as his arm would reach, Steve slowly poured the batter all over my erect cock. Pulling the waistband up to my naval, he slapped his hand down on the whole mess and rubbed it around.

I ejaculated into my already soiled underwear, and slapped the last pie in my own face. The mirror over the sink would have made a great photograph, reflecting this skinny, long-haired kid covered with food stuff. There was a certain point when it looked more like war paint than a sight gag. Rinsing off, my skin just glowed. Watching all these different colors slide off my body was a turn-on all its own.

Although the fact that food is the "weapon" makes this fantasy bizarre, it turns out to be a benign masochistic daydream.

Instead of blood and bruises, it's pancake batter and cake, but our hero is still immortalized in the fantasy of a photograph "reflecting this skinny, long-haired kid covered with food stuff."

Bisexual Twist

Here's one of the most creative fantasies I've ever heard. In the previous chapter, we discussed Jim, from Syracuse, in which metal rods were inserted in his and his partner's penises. In this way, he was able to have his "vagina" penetrated by a man. In the following fantasy, Jim and his partner "perform cunnilingus" on each other:

"Nearly all of my fantasies dispense with details leading up to events; I find myself already engaged when a dream begins—and it gets right to the point. This particular dream found me and another guy fondling each other's magnificent balls and sucking each other's big-headed, ample cocks while lying in the 69 position on the couch.

"Within minutes of this exciting encounter, we both realized we could make our tongues very slender and very long—about the diameter of a fat, round lead pencil. As he sucked my very hard cock between his lips, I could feel his special tongue probing my piss-slit—then farther and farther into my urethra.

"I could do the same, and was able to taste his sweet pre-cum on my tongue every time I withdrew it from his cock. As I slowly slid my tongue down into his urethra, I could feel its narrowing and widening as it directed me ever closer toward his prostate. I could feel his Cowper's glands pumping sweet juices and could bend the tip of my tongue to play in the openings—stimulating yet more.

"I could feel his tongue reaching into my previously unexplored urethral recesses, and then it arrived at my prostate.

He gently thrust it in and out of the narrowing while having my cock-head and shaft completely engulfed tightly in his mouth. For the first time, I felt like every inch of my manhood—inside and out—was experiencing complete sexual pleasure. And it was an equal pleasure to be providing him with what must have been similar sensations.

"As he probed and pushed through my prostatic opening with his tongue, I could feel the urge to piss and come at the same time, and my prostate responded with pleasurable convulsions. We withdrew our tongues completely several times, keeping cocks in our mouths to taste and swallow each other's floods of juices. And we gently squeezed and massaged each other's balls the whole time.

"We played like this for a long time before we sensed each other's labored breathing, and realized we were about to ejaculate at the same time. We increased our probing of each other's prostates and we could feel the hot semen being pumped against tongues as it made its way to our mouths. It was a fantastic sensation, having my tongue squeezed rhythmically by his prostate and bathed with sweet semen at every contraction. For these few minutes we had become 'connected' in a most complete new way."

—Jim, Syracuse

Animals

R. E. L. Masters, writing in *Sexual Self-Stimulation*, describes a 31-year-old man who, as a child, masturbated while watching two dogs have sex. Since then, "the patient has often entertained zoophilic masturbatory fantasies, visualizing, during his masturbation, 'a dog with a very long penis.' Sometimes he visualized himself as performing fellatio on a dog; at other times he fancied the dog licking his own (the patient's) penis."

The patient said he felt mild guilt because, "I often produced in myself these fantasies during coitus with my wife, and they always made me very strong and potent."[1]

Back when we lived under common law, bestiality, one form of sodomy, was illegal because it could not lead to procreation. Now, it's often punished under cruelty to animals statutes. The problem, of course, is in finding an animal that would testify that someone who gave him or her an orgasm was being cruel. At least 21 states have no laws at all against sex with animals. But in both Mississippi and Louisiana, "it is a felony to engage in the detestable and abominable crime against nature committed with a [nonhuman] beast.

I've known both men and women who, for whatever reason (curiosity and loneliness are the most common), have smeared peanut butter, jelly and other assorted delicacies including canned tuna on their genitals to attract the attention of a pet dog or cat. I know of *no one* who actually *preferred* a dog—unless she was married to him. Animals often appear in fantasies, but they're usually sadistic in nature, a man fantasizing that he's forcing a woman to service an animal, for example.

Risk and Danger

Once again, it's the effort to bring variety to sex that leads to this unusual type of fantasy. As Robert Stoller, M.D. writes, "Sexual boredom is, I believe, especially the result of the loss of sense of risk. So, even if the other proper elements are present in the fantasy/pornography, it does not work well unless one can still be just a bit fearful, uncertain of a successful outcome."[2]

Stoller's point is that a sense of risk or danger may be essential to good sex and good sex fantasies. We've certainly found "danger" in masochistic, sadistic, exhibitionistic, voyeuristic, and other fantasies. But Stoller points out a paradox: While the fantasy must be realistic enough to create a twinge of anxiety regarding the danger, if it's too realistic, creating considerable anxiety, it will destroy the lust value of the fantasy. Says Stoller, "One must reduce anxiety without also ending excitement. This is done by infusing a *sense* of risk into the story; in reality, the risk cannot be great or anxiety will arise. One can only have the impression of risk."

"I read somewhere that there are people into skydiving nude," writes Jerry from Iowa. "So I fantasized that I signed up for a nude skydiving course, and there was this beautiful woman with long brown hair and big breasts who was in the class. We decided to jump together, and on the way down I drifted over and we had the most wonderful fuck.

"But then, when I was really getting into the fantasy, really turned on and about to cum, I realized that our parachutes would get tangled up and probably collapse, and we'd end up dead. So I started to lose my erection, because I really didn't want to die, just get screwed. So then I figured out that we would have about two and a half minutes of free fall before we'd have to release the parachute. Then I had us leaping out of the plane already going at it, and that was great—spinning through space with my arms and legs around her, my cock in her. This is one of those fantasies I can go back to over and over. And if it's really feeling good, hell, we'll just hit the ground. Is there a better way to go? But usually we pull the chutes just in time."

More frequently than you might expect, danger fantasies might actually end in the daydreamer's death. In literature and film as well as private fantasy, the theme of sex and death appears frequently. Why are the two linked in the human mind? Death is unacceptable—even intolerable—only to the self-conscious individual. Caught up in the transcendent joy of sex, one loses one's individuality, one's selfhood, and becomes dissolved in pleasure or ecstasy. Throughout historys sex and ecstatic religions have been the handmaidens of death, gently leading us to the consummation of the marriage.

Erotic risk taking, danger, and death fantasies are not at all like violent movies in that, while blood may be shed, the spotlight isn't on pain and suffering. Should the starring victim of the fantasy scream, that would introduce the anxiety that Stoller says could bring the show to an immediate halt. The fantasizer isn't dealing with pain but with death. He can lose himself in ecstasy and slip into death. Remaining conscious of pain while experiencing the pleasure of orgasm is another story, and may well be impossible.

Part I of this book dealt with the most common sexual fantasies, as well as some that are not so common. We traced the qualities that they have in common, whether they involve sex with a stranger, orgies or brutal scenes. All fantasies fulfill some basic and rather simple human needs. We talked about what they are, and what our fantasies say about us.

In Part II, we'll find out how to use fantasies to improve our lives—and how to improve the fantasies themselves.

PART II

BETTER LIVING
THROUGH FANTASY

CHAPTER IX

Restoring Sex to Partnerships

After the mandatory bit of foreplay, you climb into the saddle and are racing like hell toward the finish line. She moans in pleasure, and you feel an even greater surge of masculine potency. Her eyes are closed, her mouth open. She's breathing heavily. It looks as though you may both surge to victory simultaneously.

But if you could read her mind at that moment, you might suffer grave disappointment. Those fingernails might not be raking *your* back. The name she's whispering under his breath could well be Robert Redford, Tom Hanks—or even Jodi Foster. Chances are three to one she's lost in fantasy, and the odds are it doesn't involve you.[1]

Why does she choose to flee this supreme moment in your embrace to shack up with an imaginary lover? For the very reasons you're probably doing the same. The good news is that those fantasies may keep the sexual aspect of a relationship together when otherwise it would fail. Here are some reasons that we turn to fantasies even when we're in bed with a real live flesh-and-blood human being whom we love.

Overcoming Boredom

"The constraints of monogamy, the annoyances of everyday family problems and the monotony of well established routines may, in time, place a damper on sexual responsiveness. To recapture the romance experienced during the courtship and early marriage, some wives turn to other men (and their husbands turn to other women)." So says Marc H. Hollender, M.D., in an article on women's sexual fantasies.[2]

The truth is the truth, and it doesn't go away because we deny or ignore it: Most long-term sexual relationships eventually grow tiresome. That's one reason people strike up extramarital affairs. Or divorce. Or seek counseling. Such advice as to change the sexual environment (for example having sex on the kitchen table or living room floor or your teenage son's or daughter's bed) can actually work—until that, too, becomes boring. A counselor might say, "The two of you aren't getting into each other deeply enough." or, "One of you is holding something back," or, "If you loved each other on a more total level," or, "If you just surrendered your lives to God," everything will work out. For the most part,' taint so. Hate the fact if you want to, but face it: Boredom is the usual result of long-term relationships.

Which is not to say it's inevitable.

"Ralph and I have lived together for 27 years," says

Bryan, a middle-aged gay man. Ralph, ten years Bryan's senior, consciously strove to keep the erotic aspect of the relationship fresh and imaginative. Still, after a decade, Bryan began to experience wanderlust.

"That's when I started turning to fantasy," Bryan said. "Maybe it was the check-out boy at the supermarket. Sometimes a cute hunk on TV. A few times it was even a boyish looking woman at the office. I call that my hetero phase. If Ralph ever knew I made believe he was a woman, he'd probably drop dead of shock. But fantasies like that keep me from being bored."

Avoiding Negative Reality

Sometimes the reality of a lovemaking scene is simply unpleasant. Perhaps the partner is inebriated, or has behaved unacceptedly, or insists on sleeping though all the fun. Fantasy can replace the jerk with a new and improved model. A 32-year-old married woman told Dr. William Masters how she "punished" her husband with a fantasy: "My husband and I had a lousy sex life for years, and it mirrored a lousy relationship. During this time, my sex fantasies almost always involved making it with other men while he was forced to watch me with great humiliation. It was sweet revenge, I guess."[3]

"I guess my wife got bored with our sex life," says a correspondent from Scranton, Pennsylvania. "We were married about four years. She was a waitress in a diner and got off at 11:00 p.m. It took her about 20 minutes to get home, but some nights she didn't get in until two or three in the morning. It didn't take a rocket scientist to see through her flimsy excuses, and she finally admitted that she met this guy at the diner and they were fucking.

"For a couple of weeks I couldn't even get it up for her, even when she wanted to. (I think she was feeling guilty.) Then one night when she had off, we started fooling around. I got it into my head that I was this other guy, while the real me was tied to a chair. They were going to torture me with jealousy until I couldn't take it anymore and killed myself so they could be together. But inside, I was actually the other guy. I touched her in all the soft, exciting ways I knew she loved—her inner thighs, the backs of her knees. I nibbled at her ears. I touched the tip of my dick all around her vaginal area, brushed it softly over her clitoris. In the real world, I played with her for 20 minutes, hard as a rock. In the fantasy, she looked over at me tied to the chair. Her face was flushed, her eyes narrow when she said, 'Oh, he's so good, so good. Look how big his cock is. We're both high, baby, so high. And now he's gonna put it in me.'

"And that's what I did. I slid it in her, and she was more juicy than I'd ever experienced before. We had one hell of a time that night, and a few weeks later she told me it was all over with the guy from the diner. The important thing is, I've been using that same fantasy for eleven years, with a few variations. Like sometimes she'll come over and play with me while he's screwing her from behind. Sometimes she'll be cruel and mutilate me. Actually give my balls as a present to her lover. But fantasizing that I'm this other guy has definitely improved our sex lives, no two ways about it."

Creating a More Erotic Scene

"I've been married to my wife for 28 years," says another correspondent. "I love her today more than ever. I would literally sacrifice my life for her. But we've probably had sex a thousand times, starting a year before we were married, and I don't think there was a single time I didn't use fantasy to get off. And the same is probably true of her. Not that she fantasized every time, because she didn't have orgasms every time. But I'm pretty sure that when she got off it was because of fantasy."

The fantasies this man entertained include a younger woman, usually in her mid-teens, always with a voluptuous figure, sadistic men and women forcing him to serve them, his real-life wife having sex with another man while he is obligated to watch, and sadistic daydreams in which he forces his wife to service another man and him simultaneously.

Naive romantics and pietists may go on proclaiming that even *fantasies* of infidelity are to be condemned. But, reality being what it is, we can be sure that even the condemners are either fantasizing when they have sex, or acting out their fantasies in reality. Dr. Hollender tells of a woman who, like many others, retreated to a modified rape fantasy because, she said, "I think it probably helped me to have an orgasm when I might not have otherwise had one." The key to her sexual response was the feeling that she was being taken forcefully and used brutally. "My husband just isn't a very violent person," she explained. So, when they had sex she pretended that he was a brute of a man who used her virtually as a masturbation device.

Another woman with a similar favorite fantasy said that she could be aroused only if she were made to feel "weaker, feminine, helpless, and that I can be taken and used." In reality, she found the idea repugnant, but as fantasy it allowed her to assume a very feminine role and become sexually responsive.[4]

Being in Control

I've said previously that power is indispensable in erotic fantasies. One important purpose of the sexual fantasy is to bestow power on the daydreamer. Hollender relates the story of a woman who, during sexual intercourse with her husband, fantasized that she was masturbating. "She had enjoyed sexual relations more when she was first married because her husband was then shy and unaggressive.... By changing the nature of the act—from coitus to masturbation, and eliminating her partner, she maintained control..."[5]

A correspondent in his mid-20's relates a masturbation fantasy of which he is *not even aware*:

"I'm writing for your fantasy book. I have been married for five years, and my wife and I have great sex at least once or twice every day. And I can tell you for sure I don't need fantasies.

"From the beginning, I asked my wife to lay there quietly and don't move. I lube up and put my cock in her, and then move real slow. I get my ass up high and then slide deep into her, then pull out with my ass in the air again, and back down. I can see in my head what it would look like, watching me slowly fuck. (I've got a great body!) I don't think at all about my wife. It's like she's just a hole in the mattress. I just concentrate on the feeling, and what it must look like. In fact, I've actually put mirrors against the wall so I can watch myself fucking.

"Of course, after I come, and the edge is off my horniness, I spend lots of time going down on my wife, petting her, and getting her off maybe two or three times."

This fellow says more than he realizes when he equates his wife with a hole in a mattress. In order to remain totally in control and sexually all-powerful, he eliminates his wife from the act entirely. But he's mistaken in assuming that he has no sexual fantasy. In fact, he's performing before an audience, imagining—and sometimes actually observing—what he looks like to the crowd while his naked body is engaged in sex.

Of course the more obvious control fantasies involve bondage and other forms of dominance. A man may be intimidated by his wife's career success or aggressiveness. He still loves her, and doesn't want to complicate or risk the relationship by having an affair with a more demure, submissive woman, yet he is unable to maintain potency with his wife. Suddenly one evening a fantasy springs from his unconscious. He imagines himself using his physical superiority to overwhelm the woman. He ties her naked and spread-eagled to a bed and begins tickling her inner thighs with a feather. She twists and giggles. "Stop it!" she demands, but he continues.

He kneels between her legs and with his tongue caresses her labia. He notices the increased rate of her breathing and very gently tickles the base of her clitoris. She moans.

"Come on baby, what do you want? Beg for it," he demands. Stubbornly, she says nothing. Again, he laps very gently. She begins thrashing her head from side to side. "Beg!" he demands. And finally, she does, whimpering, "Please. Please!"

This fantasy plays out as he caresses his wife's body in reality. By the time she's ready for his penetration, he's surging with desire and potency.

So far we've been talking about what might be called "secret" fantasies—those indulged in by one partner and not shared with the other. Such fantasies are extremely common, so much so that those in long-term relationships who do *not* have them actually constitute a minority. Although to my knowledge the question has never been researched professionally, I firmly believe that when both partners in a long-term relationship enjoy a rich erotic fantasy life, chances of sustaining the relationship are higher than average. (About 52 percent of marriages end in divorce.)

The only risk in having secret sex fantasies is a guilt reaction. Hollender described a woman who was unable to reach orgasm until she found her "perfect" fantasies, which were "of a pseudomasochistic nature...in which she would see herself being abused by her husband while other men look on. "The fantasies stimulated her passions, but they were so vivid in her imagination that she felt overwhelming shame and in real life demanded that her husband stop having coitus with her."

Millions of people, like this woman, don't have the wherewithal to confront with common sense the sex negativism that was instilled in them as children. They damage their own emotional stability by fluctuating between a life of unrestrained hedonism and sexual guilt and shame. The end of that road is clinical depression at best. If you have moral or ethical problems with secret erotic fantasies, such daydreams are probably best avoided. But if they don't raise a dilemma, they can bring joy and freshness to your sex life.

Sharing Erotic Fantasies

What a marvelous step forward it can be in a total relationship to share sexual fantasies! It's not easy for most people because it means saying, in effect, "There's something you don't know about me. When we make love I sometimes have this sexual fantasy. I want to share it with you, but I don't want you to think I'm weird or anything."

In fact, it may be weird indeed. The late sex therapist Helen Singer Kaplan, M.D., told of a married couple who came to her complaining that, although they had been married for six months, they still hadn't consummated the relationship. The husband confessed that, although he was totally impotent in his wife's presence, he was able to achieve erection and masturbate easily when alone.

For a while, therapy achieved nothing. Finally, Kaplan questioned the man about his masturbatory fantasies. At first he was reluctant to discuss them, but "finally admitted, with great shame and obvious fear that he would be rejected by his wife, that as a boy he had had a Superman masturbatory fantasy which aroused him greatly. In fact, when he was an adolescent he had actually bought a Superman costume and would pretend to rescue women who were being harassed by brutal men while he masturbated to orgasm."

Kaplan advised the couple to go home and have sex while the man indulged without shame or guilt in his Superman fantasies. They returned to Kaplan's office the following week astounded. Mrs. D, rather than responding negatively, found herself actually "turned on" by the notion that her husband would have such heroic fantasies while masturbating. Finally, Mr. D "was given permission by the therapist to buy a Superman suit for the occasion if he liked and his wife agreed to this without any evidence of reluctance. He laughingly refused, but he did employ a fantasy to dispel his anxiety during the initial coital experience which took place successfully that night."[6]

Yes, some fantasies are really weird. Yet, most people are much more tolerant of idiosyncrasy than they're given credit for. I think that's especially true of women; men typically are the ones with all the answers. Women are less judgmental because, on the whole, they recognize a broader diversity of truth than men traditionally do. Actually, no women whose husbands or lovers revealed the following fantasies, condemned them. In fact they willingly, if not ecstatically, shared in acting them out:

—The man's fantasy was to suck another man's penis. The woman bought a life-sized latex penis at an adult toy shop, had the man lie on his back in bed, and thrust the device in and out of his mouth while riding him to orgasm. She found it particularly satisfying: "I had such a sense of power forcing my husband to suck another man's cock!"

—The man fantasized being a sex slave. One Saturday morning the woman led him naked to the back porch, where anyone coming into the yard would see him, tied his hands and legs to the railing and left him there for an hour before taking him up to the bedroom and forcing him to satisfy her.

—He wanted to have public sex. She masturbated him to orgasm in a public swimming pool.

—He wanted to be diapered. She powdered his butt, patted it gently and diapered him.

—He wanted to be spanked. She spanked him roughly, playing with his phallus.

"Rachel" Miller is a transvestite, which means that, although completely heterosexual, he nonetheless finds great pleasure dressing and passing as a woman. For years he did this behind his wife's back, but, as he writes in his autobiography, *The Bliss of Becoming One*, "In time my fears began to mutate into growing feelings of self-confidence. I felt good enough about myself to finally tell my wife about my transvestism. It was a difficult step, but taking it removed a tremendous burden. I no longer had to sneak around trying to get a small taste of cross-dressing. I quit hiding my clothes and moved them into our closet. I began wearing my sexiest outfits to bed on a regular basis. At times I got completely dressed and made up, and my wife and I spent the evening together. Our sex life improved."[7]

Rachel and his wife "began to explore ways that both of us could wear sexy lingerie... Wearing lingerie became a release for my sexual inhibitions and provided a harmless, even desirable, avenue for long-suppressed exhibitionism."[8]

Of course, acting out a fantasy together risks the same unpleasant result as acting it out alone: The fantasy is usually much more satisfying than the reality. In fact, Brenda Love, who writes and lectures regularly on human sexuality, says, "Contrary to what most people believe, it is not advisable to act out a person's favorite masturbation fantasy. This is because reality with its physical limitations can never match the diverse activity and timing possible in the mind. A person can easily come to have unrealistic expectations in regard to their favorite fantasy and will often be disappointed or perhaps even blame the partner for a sloppy performance." Love recommends creating a *new* fantasy that will lend itself to reenactment in the real world. (She lists as among the most popular acting out fantasies abduction, burglary, sex slave, rape, military games, prison, pirates, college fraternity initiations, police arrest, Indian capture, and space ships!)[9]

A compromise that works well for some couples is to *spontaneously* create fantasies during foreplay or coitus:

Woman—Let's pretend Bill is in bed with us.

Man—Do you have the hots for Bill?

Woman—It's just a fantasy.

Man—What do you want to do with him?

Woman—I want *you* to suck his cock. I'm gonna guide it right into your mouth.

Man—Why?

Woman—Because I want you to be my sex slave and do everything I ask.

Man—I've never fooled around with a guy. I'm not queer.

Woman—You'll be queer if I tell you to be. You'll do

whatever I say. He's standing in front of you right now. Open your mouth. Keep screwing me, just open your mouth. (Reluctantly the male opens his mouth wide.) Suck him. Go ahead, I want to see your head move. (The man obliges.) Now lick his balls. (He pretends to do so, pumping harder.) That's good. Now make him cum.

The potential for these mutually constructed fantasies is infinite. In the process, an important phenomenon takes place. Partners whose sexual turn-ons might be quite different move toward a common ground and co-create scenes with erotic energy that both can enjoy. Here, intimate and vulnerable to each other, they find that they can bond on yet another level, more intimate, even, than the sex act itself, for it combines sex with the sharing of secrets at the deepest levels of their personalities.

CHAPTER X

Healing Through Fantasy

The notion that the "purpose" of sex is exclusively to procreate is as mistaken and naive as the theory of an earth-centered universe. Sex is at the core of human existence. It's central to our equilibrium, both physically and emotionally—and I think there's a good argument that it's central to our spirituality as well. It's the gyroscope that keeps us on course, prevents us from tipping over, and if we do begin to tip, sex can be the stabilizing force that puts us back in balance.

Often it exercises its influence through erotic fantasy. Keep in mind that fantasy is born in our unconscious, and only when we become conscious of what turns us on can we manipulate details and direct our sexual daydreams. Fantasies tell the truth about us, sometimes truth we don't want to know, and sometimes in a language we cannot understand. Psychoanalyst Robert Stoller says that in our most fulfilling fantasy "is summarized one's sexual life history—the development of his or her eroticism and of masculinity and femininity. In the manifest content of the fantasy are embedded clues to the traumas and frustrations inflicted on sexual desires in childhood by the outside world, the mechanisms created to assuage the resultant tension, and the character structure used to get satisfaction from one's body and the outside world."[1]

But fantasy is more than revelatory. It's also therapeutic. And often the traumas healed by erotic fantasies have nothing at all to do with sex.

Nonsexual healing through erotic fantasies

Through shared sex, solo sex, and erotic fantasies, we deal with loneliness, self-esteem, aggression, emotional trauma, and other aspects of our daily existence. Most of us understand ourselves well enough. To realize that our need for sex isn't always the same as our need for orgasm.

Loneliness. "My wife died of cancer in 1991," a man writes. "She chose to spend her last weeks at home, and we hugged and cuddled up to the end. I missed her something awful. Friends, even our kids said I should get back into circulation right away and meet somebody else, but I didn't want to do it. She was my one and only love for my whole life, and the only one I wanted.

"I thought with any luck I would just die. My heart would just stop. Then, a couple of months after she passed away, I woke up with an erection. That's the way that I woke up most mornings when she was alive, because she would reach over and start playing with me and I'd get hard. So it was natural for me to imagine her doing the same thing that morning. I could feel her hand on me, although, of course, it was my own hand. I actually felt the weight of her head on my shoulder, smelled her hair. I could even feel her breasts against my chest. That's how I got off that morning, for the first time since she left me. It's been my one and only fantasy ever since, and I'm not so lonely anymore."

Millions of men and women of all ages live alone these days. Some prefer the single lifestyle. Others have yet to meet someone with whom they wish to share their space and their lives. Still others are divorced or widowed. I've met a few people who are delighted with this solitary existence. They like themselves a great deal, enjoying entertaining themselves, and usually have high levels of self-esteem. But we're a gregarious species, and even those who don't need companionship still hunger on occasion for the warmth of another body against theirs. In the absence of physical intimacy we grow lonely. Fantasy can heal that ache.

"I travel a lot on business," writes Ronald D., a Minneapolis businessman. "My wife doesn't like being alone nights, so, being a smartass, I told her to get herself a big pillow and cuddle it. About two years ago, I came home from a trip and damned if she doesn't have this huge pillow where I sleep in our bed. She's also got this electric vibrator on the night table, right out there in the open. She tells me the pillow's name is Harvey, and he really know how to make out!"

Self-esteem. One of the most important functions of fantasy—sexual and otherwise—is to help us improve our self-esteem. In reality we might be gaunt or fat, too short or conspicuously tall, flat-chested or with breasts so large as to be embarrassing. We men might be normally endowed, yet concerned that we're a mini-meat, a puny-prick, a dinky-dick.

Especially in adolescence, we're likely to worry that no girl would be sufficiently interested in us to let us do sex things with her. And if she did, we'd be too clumsy, too shy, come across as a first-class jerk. Soon, everyone in the school would know.

Then, just before falling asleep one night, it happens: You step out of the shower in the boys' locker room after gym class and she's standing right there—the most beautiful, sparkling, big-breasted chick in the school. (Seems she made a wrong turn, although the details are unimportant.) Her eyes rivet on the ponderous, though flaccid, genitals hanging between your legs. "Gee, it's big!" she exclaims. Next thing, she's on her knees kissing—actually kissing—the tip of your cock! It springs to life instantly, a good 12 to 15 inches tall. Her eyes get wide as saucers.

"Please, take me now—take me now!" she exclaims.

From such joyous if naive adolescent fantasies is born sexual self-confidence. A young woman's concern about how she will ever entice a lover is assuaged in a fantasy in which she "accidentally" brushes her breasts against the high school quarterback's lips as she bends across his desk to sharpen a pencil. Suddenly, he's springing for Coke and a Big Mac at the Golden Arches and love is in the air.

Ultimately, through her fantasies, she begins to build confidence in her sexual appeal. She begins to practice subtle flirtation in the real world, testing her approach in fantasy. In her daydreams she may rehearse how far she wants to go, how and when to say, "No," how and when to say, "Yes."

In our fantasies, we learn to value ourselves sexually. That's the positive aspect of the narcissism and power intrinsic to erotic fantasies. And sexual self-esteem spills over into everyday life. People who are confident in their sexuality usually are confident across the board.

Confronting Trauma

One of my closest friends had a traumatic childhood in that his father, a chronic alcoholic, would, when inebriated, spend hours berating his son for no particular reason. From age 12 until he left home at 18, he recalled that virtually every night, while he attempted to sleep, his father sat drinking at the kitchen table and shouting, "I hate your guts, you little bastard!" "You lousy sissy," and scores of similar insults. The boy had a religious nature and knew that he was compelled to "honor thy father and thy mother," yet felt what he called a "pure, white hatred" for his father.

Bob was 29 years old, some years after his mother passed away, his father died in a skid row mission. The news upset him more profoundly than he could ever have imagined. He was a professional writer, and began a novel based on the relationship between his dad and himself—it was more an attempt to come to grips with this critical part of his life than to create any literary masterpiece.

As those who have done serious writing know, there comes a point when the story takes on a life of its own. It writes itself. The characters speak their own minds. And one night that's what my friend experienced. It came to him as an erotic fantasy which he quickly wrote down. It's certainly violent, and if that sort of thing troubles you, just skip to the next section. It turned out to be a breakthrough, a profound life experience for Bob, and so I present it in its entirety here:

> An eighteen-year-old boy walks slowly down the narrow stone steps of a circular stairway. He is naked, and all the muscles of his strong body bulge and ripple The boy breathes heavily. Sometimes he groans under the weight he is carrying, and the sound breaks the ominous

silence and echoes far down into the earth. He feels the sweat running down his chest and thighs. His heartbeat thuds in his ears.

Finally the steps funnel into a corridor so narrow the boy must walk sideways to move through it with his burden. The ceiling is low, the heat oppressive. The youth shuffles along for many minutes until he feels he must stop to rest. But at that moment the gleam of his flickering lantern is reflected in the iron bars of the cell door where the passage ends.

The young man grasps the latch and pulls the gate wide. It swings in absolute silence. The boy steps into the cell.

The ceiling is very high—the boy cannot see the top. Perhaps it was once an old cave. It seems to carry an eternal silence in its walls. From out of the darkness of the ceiling a chain hangs, and at the end, at the height of the boy's head, is a hook. He hangs the lantern on it, then rests the man gently on the floor.

He returns to the door, pulling it closed by one of the bars, because there is no handle inside. It clanks shut. Next to the door are three padlocks and three chains. He wraps the chains securely around the bars, then fastens each with a padlock. The keys hang on the wall where the locks had been. He takes them down one by one, ceremoniously, and throws them through the bars, far down the corridor.

The victim begins to stir, but remains unconscious. For an instant there is only the sound of the two men breathing. The pit of the boy's stomach knots. He lifts the man gently and carries him to the back wall, facing the door. There are two chains, both hanging over pulleys in the ceiling. At the end of each is a padded leather cuff. The boy takes the man's left hand, places the leather around his wrist and tightens it. He does the same with the right hand.

The boy turns a crank in the cell. The rusty gears screech through the silence. The victim's arms bend at the elbows and begin rising over his head in uneven jerks as though he were a marionette. When his arms grow taut and begin straining under his weight, his eyes open. He looks ahead, focusing nowhere.

The boy continues to turn the crank. To avoid the pain in his arms, the victim stands tall. But soon the slack is taken in, and again his arms are fully extended above his head. For a moment the boy stops cranking, going to the man's side to secure large leather cuffs around the victim's wide-spread ankles.

The man's body stretches an inch, two inches as the cranking resumes. His feet leave the ground and he hangs by his wrists. Still the boy cranks, until the chains at the victim's feet grow taut. The man groans in agony. His eyes are wide and black and sunk deep in his head. They roll toward the ceiling.

The body is white and bony. The hairless skin clutches the rib cage so that every rib is visible, and beneath them a profound depression plunges to the navel. Hip bones protrude like a skeleton's. The lower abdomen is flat and narrow, rooted in the dark curls of pubic hair. The genitals are large in contrast to the scrawny figure, but the legs are sinewy and wasted, tapering to big, ugly feet with bulging blue veins.

The young man locks the crank in place. He reaches beneath it to the floor and withdraws a long, thin dagger. Gingerly he touches the blade with his thumb. The knife cuts the skin and leaves a thin line of blood.

The glint of steel in the dim light catches the victim's eye and he gazes at the blade in horror. A trace of sympathy appears in the boy's face. He walks toward the agonizing sacrifice, extending the knife in his open palm before him.

"This is the knife that is going to rip you open," the boy says. But his voice is gentle, as though he is speaking of love. His eyes caress the emaciated body. "The door is locked," he says. "No one can get in here, ever, and neither of us can ever leave. We are together, and I am going to kill you."

The boy bends over and kisses the man's abdomen. Again and again he kisses the stretched white skin below the navel, then licks it clean with his tongue, nipping at the tiny hairs. He kisses the navel itself, then nuzzles his face into the depression beneath the ribs.

With the empty hand he caresses the man's sides, then slides his hands around to the cheeks of his ass and touches them tenderly.

Finally he says, "It has to be like this, you know."

The man whimpers.

For the first time he touches the old man's genitals. Briefly he pets the shaft. Then he weighs the balls, marveling at their hairy texture. He holds them for many minutes, drinking in the peace that washes over him. He fondles the penis and the balls together, feeling their warmth and sponginess.

Finally, he brings the blade of the knife to the base of the scrotum. He stares straight into the victim's wide eyes, and pulls roughly on the organs. Holding them away from the body, he quickly slashes.

The man lurches forward, his mouth wide with the screams of agony, but there is no sound. In the young man's hand dangles the oozing flesh. The boy has a strong urge to stuff the organs into the man's mouth. Instead he drops them into the puddle of blood on the floor.

The blood splashes from the wound onto the young man's body. "It will not be long now, Father," he says. Again he reaches behind the man and massages the buttocks. He traces his finger up the spine, placing the flat of his hand in the hollow of the man's back. He pulls the victim forward, and places the tip of the blade against the taut white, trembling flesh at the navel. The man tries to suck in his abdomen, to lay it flat against his spine. But the tip of the blade follows the quivering body.

The boy pushes harder and the skin parts around the very tip. The old man stares into the boy's eyes in terror, and the boy meets the gaze with tenderness.

"I am sorry, Father, I really am. I wish there could be another way." He stretches up toward the face, the castration blood spattering against his thighs. He stretches up to the man until his lips are touching those cracked and dried lips and the bodies are together, and at the same moment he eases the knife deep into the man's gut.

"Oh!" cries the victim. He tries desperately to twist away from the blade, but with the hand in the hollow of his back, he is held motionless. The chained body arches, the torso pressed against the knife, the belly swallowing the full blade up to the handle. The head drops forward, the lips still pressed against the boy's.

The boy unfastens the cuffs from the ankles and wrists and very gently rests the man on the cold stone floor. The sunken eyes stare into the young face, pleading and helpless. The boy presses close to the man and caresses the bleeding body. He grasps the handle of the knife and slowly removes the blade. Fresh blood spurts from the wound in bright red rhythms, splashing the boy. He washes his body in it, then the man's body. He climbs onto the almost lifeless form and wraps his arms around it, holding it tightly. He can still feel the blood spurting. Then the man's arms are around him, too, and they cling together.

And that is how it ends most of the time, with me drinking great pleasure from the sick image of my old man dying helpless in crimson pools of blood. But sometimes it changes, and it is I who hang cuffed to the wall, my body slashed and mutilated, my blood bathing him. It is he who lifts me from the chains, overcoming me with the strength of his body, putting me on the floor with such gentleness, me marred and sexless now, raping me and I do not even want to protest. I am dying and so there is no need to be proud, no need to fight back anymore.[2]

Bob had never intended writing that last paragraph The fantasy itself was the most erotic he had ever imagined, filling him with almost dizzying erotic power through destroying the man for whom he felt "pure, white hatred." But that's the wonder of fantasy—its ability to bring to the surface that which exists in the deepest interiors. He could have endured the years of insult and humiliation—that wasn't the point. Even to go on living wasn't the point. He needed his father to love him. It was that simple. In the fantasy, he had forced his father to yield his body, if not his love. But it could just as well go the other way. His father could have forced *him* to yield, and then, perhaps when the boy is dying, the father would finally embrace him. My friend assures me that the first and last time he ever cried over the relationship with his father was while writing that final paragraph. The tears were bitter and prolonged, but they were also cathartic, coming from a fantasy so honest that it kicked open the door to truth and obliterated a lifetime of hatred in a moment of insight.

Even as children, we entertain fantasies of aggression. What youngster, male or female, picked on by a bully, hasn't daydreamed of lying in wait on some dark and lonely road until the enemy passed by, then slugging him with a 2 x 4 and knocking him to the ground and bashing his face in with a boulder, being sure not to kill him, the point being that the bully must live with his punishment forever. That'll teach him a thing or two.

After puberty, aggression fantasies may become eroticized. The bully is raped or castrated. He may be humiliated in front of fellow students—stripped naked and found to have the most minute genitals imaginable. He may be forced to fellate other males. Such fantasies, accompanied by masturbation, are often sufficient to release the anger and aggression felt because of the real-life situation. Writes Walter Braun, M.D., "...masturbation may fulfill, in a paradoxical way, a social mission— in protecting society from extreme forms of conduct that otherwise might demand—and find—an outlet."[3] It may be that more and more teenagers seem to be bringing guns to school and killing their enemies because they haven't been taught to deal with their aggression through erotic fantasy and masturbation.

Sometimes, as you'll remember, the fantasizer reverses roles. While masturbating, he may handle his genitals roughly — pinching, squeezing, or slapping. Isidor Bernstein writes of a patient who "always felt pleasure at minor pains inflicted on himself. He masturbated with the aid of a scrub brush in such a way that the bristles would create a stabbing sensation. He rationalized this masochistic behavior on the grounds that it made him feel more alive... He also had masturbation fantasies of beautiful girls who were tied so that they would be helpless while he did sexual things to them, especially pump water into their vaginas."[4]

When the roles are reversed, usually it's because, even in fantasy, the daydreamer can't permit himself the acts of brutality that he unconsciously yearns to perform. Remember that my friend, who as a child was religious, did not fantasize revenge until a decade later, when his religious views had changed radically.

Kerry Kelly Novick and Jack Novick, Ph.D., of the Michigan Psychoanalytic Institute, tell of a boy named Abel, who had fantasies of being beaten by older boys, pop singers, and football players, "but also masturbated with fantasies of having his penis and testicles burned or otherwise damaged. Further masturbation fantasies involved death and suicide..." Such fantasies seem to bring about a diminution of anxiety..."[5]

Abel may have had violent anger reactions to some of the boys at school who picked on him, but, since his conscience would not let him destroy them, even in fantasy, he, identifying with them, destroyed himself. As Isador Bernstein points out, "Through the repeated intimate and reassuring association of the recall of the traumatic event and the sexual excitement of the masturbation, the event takes on an erotic flavor.... The sexualization of the trauma is an additional means of mastery."[6]

Sexual healing through erotic fantasy

I believe that even the most violent and gruesome fantasies serve a crucial function as long as there is no desire to act them out in reality. *The erotic fantasy tells us what is already inside us.* It's absolutely essential to understand that. Fantasies don't *create* who we are—they *reveal* who we are. They help us to know ourselves. Then, if we find something in ourselves that we wish to change, at least we know where to start. Here are a couple of areas in which fantasies have helped:

Low sex drive. Perhaps that term—low sex drive—isn't accurate. Especially when applied to women, it suggests that there's something not quite normal about how long it takes them to become aroused sexually. Men are ready to get it going and get it over with in 30 seconds flat. Does she have a low sex drive, or is he suffering from hypersexuality?

The point is that some women, especially those whose partners make a real effort to get them involved, really do want to reach orgasm, and a recent study of 212 married women found that sex fantasies helped many of them do just that.[7]

Even women who have been anorgasmic—unable to achieve orgasm—all their lives can do so with the help of fantasies. Joseph LoPiccolo, Ph.D., and colleagues treated one woman who masturbated for 45 continuous minutes before, with the assistance of fantasy, finally reaching an orgasm for the first time in her life. Says LoPiccolo, "Interestingly, the concept of fantasizing during masturbation does not seem to occur spontaneously to our female clients."[8]

Functional Impotence. Although Viagra, MUSE, and several other drugs can now create erections on demand, even in some cases where the cause is organic, or physical, the price of those drugs limits their use for many men. Often, an improved, richer fantasy life can help solve the problem.

I've already discussed how *boredom* can ruin one's sex life. Nothing's to be gained by denying the truth; we can become bored with a partner, a position, a place, even a fantasy. We say to ourselves, "It just doesn't turn me on anymore." And of course if a man isn't turned on, he's impotent— sexually dysfunctional, if that sounds less traumatic.

Also, millions of men are impotent because of *performance anxiety*—they can't get their minds off the fact that they're expected to have erections, *must* have erections or suffer enormous embarrassment, and unspoken questions about their masculinity. Go ahead, just *try* to get an erection under a psychological burden like that.

In both cases, total concentration on an effective fantasy can do the trick. Advises Dr. Charles Silverstein regarding concern over the flaccid phallus, "Stop monitoring its moment by moment state. To cut off this awareness without a new distraction to take its place is impossible; you need to shift your attention elsewhere, to sex fantasies, to recollections of hot scenes or to pictures you've seen in pornography magazines." [9]

A few years ago I received a letter from a man who said, "Thank you for your two chapters on fantasies in *The Joy of Solo Sex*. My wife and I have been married for two years, and unless I had a few drinks, I've never been able to get really stiff with her. Strangely, I've never had trouble with masturbation, which is why I bought your book. That's when I suggested to my wife that we fantasize while having sex.

"Well, it has made all the difference. The other night I was on my back and she was on top, and she put a pillow over my face, not to suffocate me, but, she said, I was nothing but her masturbation tool, and boy was that exciting.

"We do a lot of kinky things, stuff I won't even tell you about. But the fantasies have changed our sex lives forever. Thank you."

I wrote to this gentleman asking for a few more details. When did he first notice the problem? Did he have it with other partners? What does he think about while having sex with his wife when he isn't fantasizing? As I'd suspected, he had been experiencing performance anxiety.

Before he met his wife she had enjoyed a lot more sexual experience than he had. Also, she had a Ph.D. and was a professional educator; he was a junior level executive at a small company. From the beginning, he felt that he could not live up to her standards and the performance of her previous lovers. Fortunately, she was a very attractive and sensual woman, and knew how to arouse him, especially after he had a few drinks. Still, he rarely focused on sex, being preoccupied with the fact that he must achieve. The masochistic fantasy, especially when it was acted out, forced him to abandon his thoughts. He was merely a body being used.

Dr. Helen Singer Kaplan has written that, in her sex therapy programs, "Despite our attempts to alleviate pressure, some patients continue to be preoccupied with their performance: 'Will treatment work?' 'Is my erection as firm as it used to be?' 'Will it go down?' etc. Not surprisingly, such thoughts are usually accompanied by anxiety, and so they interfere with potency. Many techniques have been devised to 'distract the distracter' or 'self-observer.'" Frequently, Kaplan instructs these men to withdraw into their favorite sexual fantasies.[10]

According to Kaplan, "Erotic fantasy is the ideal distraction in that it is simultaneously a distraction and a source of stimulation..."[11]

A Safety Valve

Obviously, a great many erotic fantasies involve themes that would be unwise to act out. For example, a man might be deeply attracted to his boss's wife, yet understand that to proposition her could lead to his being fired. Or he may work with a woman (or a man for that matter) whose body turns him on, but whose personality leaves him cold. In any number of circumstances, doing the deed in the flesh may prove disastrous, but the desire can still be fulfilled in fantasy.

The same is true of desires the fulfillment of which is illegal. Lukianowicz writes of a man named Tardieu, "who for years masturbated seven or eight times daily, 'his fantasy dwelling on the outraging of female corpses...'"[12]

Curiously, Lukianowicz uses this case as an example that failed to serve as a safety valve, pointing out that, "One day he committed such a crime." In fact, the truth seems obvious: "For years" the fantasy *did* seem to function as an effective substitute for acting out.

Here's another example presented by Lukianowicz:

"A 44-year-old schoolmaster, separated, father of two children, has been all his life a professed homosexual, with a particular predilection for young boys. In spite of being heterosexually adequate, he always sought after homosexual outlets. This behavior led to his separation. Yet he managed "to keep myself out of any trouble with the police," mostly by contenting himself with masturbation accompanied by visually vivid homosexual fantasies. In them he "saw" naked adolescent boys, with their penises stiffly erected, parading in front of him. As he progressed in his masturbation, the penises of the boys increased in size, till finally the whole field of his vision was filled with one huge, erect, pulsating penis, and then the patient would have a prolonged orgasm. This type of homosexual masturbatory fantasy started shortly after his first homosexual experience, which he had at the age of ten, and it persists unchanged hitherto."[13]

The fantasy reveals strong pedophilic tendencies. Yet, there's no evidence that the man actually committed such acts —in part, no doubt, because the fantasy itself created sufficient arousal to produce orgasm.

Here's a similar fantasy written by a *CTS* reader:

About my fantasy with my young cousin. In real life I had an excellent relationship with him. A strong affection has existed since the time he was five years old. His parents were always supportive of this. I am 20 years older than my cousin. He was bright, precocious, and very cute.

He liked to arrange my hands around his belly as he sat on my lap. One time he started gyrating his bottom, I think quite aware of the erection he created. I, at the same time, found the experience exciting and horrifying, but I didn't on any occasion encourage sexual activity.

Many times back then while I was visiting his family for a weekend, he would come into my bedroom about two hours before anyone arose. He'd snuggle up to me really close. Often I would massage his back and neck (more like tickling). He was wild for this.

During his teen years, I saw him less frequently. He was usually out with his friends and kind of withdrew from adults as that age often does. At age 20, I seemed to start to develop a new closeness with him. He's always very friendly and engaging. We have many memories of the past years. He soon will be 30 years old, and appears to be straight with many girlfriends in his past.

At my age of 50 years, I find I use fantasy more and more to aid masturbation. I occasionally have a fantasy about my then young cousin of 11 years. He comes into the guest room where I'm sleeping. It's about 5 a.m. He snuggles up close to me, as he has done so many times in the past. I groggily awaken with my customary erection. He wears only white jockey shorts as usual. I'm naked under the sheets. He very decidedly presses his rear against my hard on. I feel a mild preorgasmic sensation in my cock. For about a minute he moves his rear all around, slowly stimulating my cock. I'm very nervous and quite aroused. My hand, from the beginning, is on his bare belly. I can feel the waist band of the jockey shorts. He then moves to lie flat on his back, on the bed. He pulls down his shorts in front with his other hand. I feel an impulse to move down and lick his cock all over. I follow the impulse.

He squirms and his dick twitches. I then quickly insert it into my hot, moist mouth. I start running my tongue all around his dick. He says, "Oh, that feels so good, don't stop!" So I lavish it with hot, slippery attention for a few minutes. He then arches his back slightly and says something "wild" is happening! He holds his body stiff. His dick starts throbbing in my mouth. I realize that he's orgasming; pre-pubescent orgasming. Everything but the cream. We hold our position for a few seconds. His young body goes weak and he quickly retracts his newly broken-in dick from my mouth. After we sleep for awhile he tells me that that was his first time getting off. In real life, I'm stroking my rod and my climax usually occurs about when his does, all in my fantasy.

Legendary sexologist Wilhelm Stekel has argued that

masturbation and the fantasies accompanying it are "man's best defensive measure against the outbreak of his pedophilia," because "so long as he masturbates he abstains from acting out his forbidden fantasies."[14]

A survey of sex offenders conducted by the Kinsey Institute found that men who are in prison for committing sex crimes often have mediocre sex fantasy lives. As many as 18 percent reported never having fantasized at all. Even among voyeurs and exhibitionists, who reported the greatest number of fantasies, only 20 percent to 35 percent fantasized about performing the crimes they committed.[15]

A more recent study, "The Prevalence of Sex Offenders With Deviant Fantasies," reached the same conclusion: "The frequencies of deviant fantasies for all groups tended to be low, and controls (men who were not sex offenders) had more fantasies in general than sex offenders."[16]

Although it isn't likely to happen any time soon in the United States, I expect that one or more European countries will soon begin conditioning sex offenders in the art of having vivid, detailed, "real" erotic fantasies of the criminal behavior that has put them behind bars. It's very likely that the major difference between them and the rest of us is that men who don't commit sex crimes are capable of fantasizing to orgasm the acts that criminals must *perform* in order to reach orgasm because they lack the capacity to imagine.

Spiritual healing through erotic fantasies

Sex-negative religious dogma has created serious sex problems for millions of people. In many cases, they extend through entire lifetimes of erotic malnourishment. Quite often, however, as we mature, we're hurled into an emotional civil war between God and the gonads, and the gonads triumph. The victory can take on actual physical dimensions; I've received several letters like the following: "I have a Bible with tissue-thin pages. Every time I jack off, I use one of the pages to wipe my prick, then use the semen-soaked wad to 'clean' a picture of Jesus left me by my parents. The first time I did this, I nearly laughed my head off—and I still get a charge from it."

A few months before that, another reader wrote of a similar act. (I referred to it briefly in a previous chapter.) He said, in effect, "Whenever I stay at a hotel that has a Gideon Bible in the night stand drawer, I take it out, open it on my bed and masturbate into the pages. It's a real turn-on to imagine some pious person—woman or man— opening it and finding the seed of my lasciviousness disgracing their Holy Book."

On the surface, that might seem to some an intolerable act of blasphemy, and for that reason I don't condone it. But the fact is, such acts usually are an effort of the flesh to assert itself. Those whose sexuality was most suppressed in childhood and youth by negative religious teachings are likely to require the most radical triumphing over that suppression later in life. Thus, we find Sade expressing his sexuality through the most violent anti-Christian acts and rhetoric. "Defiling" the Bible with semen is not so much an attack on religion as it is a triumphing of one's sexuality over a radical sex-negativism of a *specific* "religion."

The paper of those "defiled" Bibles is made by International Paper and other companies, not God. It is not sacred. The print is applied to those pages in printing plants. It, too, is not sacred. Physically, it is a book like any other book, and ejaculating into it is sometimes much more a political/philosophical statement than it is an act of blasphemy. It takes on the function of a fantasy in that it helps the man to perform sexually, to triumph over what must certainly have been a psychologically castrating religion-based upbringing. This is pure and simple sex triumphing over sex-negativism. I'll close this chapter with two fantasies that serve the same purposes.

My Sexy Priest

There is a young, virile priest who frequents the local health club. He is in his mid-thirties, tall, lean, well-muscled, and groomed impeccably. He's athletic and nicely tanned. He's an Air Force Reserve Chaplain one month a year, so he wears his hair short in the military way, high and tight.

He always comes dressed for his work-out in gym shorts and a muscle tee which nicely defines tight glutes, quads, pecs, and biceps. He does the entire circuit of weights and ends his visit with a hard and fast swim.

The shower is an open stall and has about ten heads. It's here I fantasize that we meet, eyes first, before giving each other an entire head-to-toe approving look. I am pleased with what I see; this man of the cloth is beautiful. He is uncut as I am, and has a large (six inches, at least) flaccid cock and big pendulous balls between his Speedo tan-lined legs. I try to look away, but cannot; I must feast my eyes on this classic V-shaped Adonis.

We both soap up, paying close attention to our cocks; he shows me how he retracts his foreskin so he can clean the corona and the glans penis and begins to jack himself, slowly at first, while looking at me. I return the look and action by pulling back my foreskin. I mimic his stroking patterns. His dick hardens to eight inches as he continues to add liquid soap to his fisting action; I am doing the same and we are intently watching each other. We are interrupted by incoming men needing to shower; we both turn ourselves toward the wall (to hide our hard-ons) and complete our showering, drying off and heading to the locker carrels. He suggests we discreetly reconvene in one of the private "family" locker rooms. He quickly pulls on a pair of nylon running shorts (minus the jock strap hanging in his locker) and I, my 501 cutoffs and a tee-shirt, and we head for the private locker room.

There he mentions he has seen me stealing admiring glances of him during his workouts. I admit I had watched from a safe distance and often fantasized about him. I tell him he is very good looking and keeps himself in great shape. He tells me that I am not so bad looking myself. He begins massaging my neck and reaches up under my shirt to run his smooth, strong hands over my chest, and pinches my now-erect nipples. His hands continue down to my straining buttoned-in bulge, squeezing and pushing it. One by one, he undoes each button of the fly, finally releasing my tumescent cock and swollen testicles. I am hot as he brings his mouth down on it, sucking in up-and-down motions; he pulls my balls as he deep throats my dick. I pull his military-cropped head down on my crotch as he expertly blows me. I let go with a potent eruption and he swallows it all.

His ballooned running shorts do not conceal his big hard-on, but I ignore this momentarily. Instead, I have him recline on the bench and pull the front of his muscle tee over his head and secure it behind his neck. I give him a full body massage, beginning with his well-formed, hairless chest, stopping at his erect nipples, twisting and pinching them; I tell him he should have either or both pierced as they are perfect in size and shape for this. He groans as I continue my downward descent massage; his abdominal muscles are hard and well-proportioned. I pass by his tented crotch, dotted with pre-cum where the tip of his still-hard penis rests. His thigh muscles are easily identifiable, as are those in his strong legs and calves; I learn he is an avid runner and biker and it shows. I have him turn over, and at the same time, I pull his shorts and muscle tee off of him. He is now lying prone, completely nude, on the bench. I rub his neck and powerful shoulders and work his back down to his bubble butt. I squeeze and pull his tight ass with up, down, and circular massage. His eyes are closed and he moans with admiration and appreciation.

By now, his cock and balls are begging for attention, and I give it to them. He is sitting on the bench with his legs spread and I am kneeling between them, stroking his powerful tool, while tugging at his huge balls. I begin mouthing the monster with my tongue and he responds by jamming the thing further down my throat and pulling my head toward him; he's watching me suck him, moaning, and moving his hips back and forth.

I grab a condom from my cutoffs, tear it open with my teeth, and with my mouth and tongue, apply it to his thick pulsing hard-on. He is watching this and cannot believe what he is seeing.

I tell him I want him to fuck me with his beautiful big cock and he obliges. I turn around, still kneeling, and position myself doggie-style, and he slides off the bench and sticks it in me, slowly at first, then fast and hard, in and out, around and around. I rock with his motions, pushing back as he pushes in.

By this time, I am hard again and he reaches around me and jacks me to his grinding motions. He explodes and then I too let go with another gusher. We shower, cleaning each other up, and exit, fully aware that our actions were far better than our admiring glances.
—W. W., CA

Communion

I am a 79-year-old grandfather who, upon discovering the mechanics involved, has masturbated at least once every day for the last 65 years. The act, along with accompanying fantasies, defines who I am—a compulsive solosexual masochistic, exhibitionistic, voyeuristic, bisexual— basically a normal and decent enough chap.

Oddly, as I became sexually active, the guilt that saturated my horny teenage brain was unrelated to the occasional fellation of my best friend Larry—natural and instinctive behavior that no one had thought to inform me was perverse. The guardians of my morals had, however, made it abundantly clear that playing with my penis was not only unmanly and morally corrupt, but physically and mentally self-destructive. And there was absolutely no way I could stop doing it.

Kneeling in church, eyes screwed shut, hands clasped in prayer, begging Jesus for help and forgiveness, I swear never, ever again. With renewed hope and resolve, I raise my eyes, see him on the cross, an exquisitely portrayed, near naked male figure. The recidivistic tingle in my groin is a humiliating reminder that inevitably my next movements in private will be spent repetitiously pulling the loose skin up over the head of my now hardening penis.

Home, and changing out of my church finery, I recognize a window of opportunity. Stroking myself, I kneel before the risen Jesus. And here my fantasy begins: I tug, and the sheet so suggestively draped about his loins falls away to nakedly reveal an aroused, godly maleness—urgent, expectant. Demanding. Grasping my penis and pulling it toward him, I slide the velvet sheathed hardness of the Savior into my mouth.

I suck.

All too swiftly, amid a final spate of frantic thrusting, he, in the sing-song cadence of our Episcopalian priest, intones, "Take, eat this in remembrance—" and ejaculates. Who needs wine, when I writhe in the euphoric throes of my own self-induced orgasm.

Contritely wiping goo from sticky fingers, I think of Jesus and Larry and fret over how many more times I will be able to jack off before it triggers some vaguely imagined but fearfully loathsome consequence.

While those whose religious views are superficial and by-the-book will abhor these fantasies, most sensitive readers will recognize in them efforts to abolish the dichotomy between the flesh and the spirit and to create the unity between both that is sorely lacking in their lives. This, too, is healing through fantasy.

CHAPTER XI

Enhancing Your Erotic Fantasy Life

Embracing your fantasies wholeheartedly can lead to increased erotic pleasure. That's because, when you're open and honest about what turns you on sexually, you can actually improve the intensity of your fantasies, making them more vivid, more real.

That's no longer based only upon subjective anecdotal testimony. Two Australian researchers, David Smith, Ph.D., and Ray Over, Ph.D., of the Department of Psychology, La Trobe University in Bundoora, set out to prove legendary sex researchers Masters and Johnson wrong when, in 1970, they wrote in *Human Sexual Inadequacy*, "No man can wish, will, or demand an erection.... Attainment of an erection [is something] over which he has absolutely no voluntary control...." Smith and Over believed that, through active use of the imagination, men could indeed have control over erections.

They chose eight heterosexual men 19 to 26 years old who had already had some experience in sexual studies. One criterion was they had to be lacking in the erotic imagination department. Another was that they all attained erections while watching erotic films. Finally, they had to have had some sexual experience.

And they had to be lucky: These guys were paid good money to think about sex and get erections!

Each man, when it was his turn to be tested, sat alone in a dimly lit, soundproof room at a comfortable temperature. He communicated with the experimenter, who was out of sight in an adjoining room, through an intercom system. He then placed a strain gauge midway along the shaft of his penis. These are very sensitive devices and can measure the slightest change in the circumference of the organ.

Next, using a prerecorded tape, the man was guided through a three-minute period of relaxation. Then there was a two-minute musical interlude to give the experimenter time to establish a baseline measure of the penis's relaxed circumference. That was followed by the actual trials: The subject was told to fantasize freely about sex subjects, or an erotic scene was described and he was told to fantasize it for two minutes. Then the subject described the intensity of his fantasy on a six-point scale ranging from vague and dim to perfectly clear and vivid. He also described his sexual response on an eleven-point scale from not sexually aroused to wildly aroused.

Each subject took the test three times—once before he was given any fantasy training, once a week after the training, and again a month after.

Now, here's where things get a little tricky. The eight men were divided evenly into two groups. One group received *general* imagery training—they focused on enhancing imaginary sights, sounds, smells, tastes, touches, a scene in which all the senses were brought to bear—but none of it having to do with sex. The other group received *sexual* imagery training, in which they concentrated on erotic themes. Both groups were given homework; the sexual training group had to fantasize pre-written sex scripts.

The results in the words of the researchers: "The present study demonstrates that voluntary control over sexual arousal can be enhanced by training men to form more vivid images.... The men who received sexual imagery training could subsequently induce tumescence [erections] under conditions of structured as well as unstructured fantasy. In contrast, participation in a program of general imagery training had no effect on subsequent sexual arousal levels under conditions of either structured or unstructured fantasy."

In other words, whether the sex scene was pre-scripted or spontaneous, men trained in enhancing sexual imagery could produce erections without touching themselves, through fantasy alone, although they were chosen for the study because they could *not* do that before the training.

One of the four men in the sexual imagery training group not only improved from training to the test, but had an even firmer erection a month later at follow-up.

In 1990, I made a statement which has been widely quoted since: "The brain is the most important sex organ." I've known men who are paraplegics—they had no feeling below the waist. Yet, they had orgasms. I have met a man who, through an accident, had lost his genitals. He experienced orgasms. That's because, ultimately, the experience of orgasm happens in the brain. Those who have experienced altered sexual states, sexual trances, psychic orgasms—in which they have had no physical contact with the genitals and yet experienced complete ejaculatory orgasms— these people have learned how to tap into the sex in their heads and, although such experiences don't appear to be very common today, entire societies have known the frenzied sexual ecstasy of this basically simple skill.

We're talking here about nothing more profound than what used to be called self-hypnosis and is now known as auto-suggestion. That's right, it is the method stage magicians use to make their subjects bark like dogs, the tool wielded by the hypnotherapist to help his patient kick the smoking habit. In each case, the subject has to accept and *entirely believe* that the suggestion being offered is in fact *real*:

It's the evening of the spring solstice. The crops have been planted, and now, in a blaze of bonfires, the thumping of drums, and chants of the high priests, the mass of virtually naked men and women spontaneously gyrate, whirl, and cry out, "Yes! Yes!" They *feel* the sexual energy welling up in them. The younger ones *know* from their observance in past years that worshippers lose their self-control, their self-identity in this frenzied night of orgiastic dancing.

In fact, they feel it emanating from the breathless, sweat-drenched bodies glistening around them in the firelight. It is a palpable force, a sex energy. It permeates the night and gnaws at the innards of all participants. It's there in the depths of their abandon, and they know—*know*—that they will become its ecstatic victim.

And so it happens, first one and then another and then by the dozens and scores. As the drumbeat becomes more persistent and the dancing more furious, one by one each falls to the ground in orgasm.

That is the power of the imagination, of accepting a suggestion as absolute truth. The critical ingredient: the conviction that the suggestion is utterly real.

That's at the heart of sexual imagery training. Following are the six steps that I've developed in order to increase the erotic impact so that virtually every man and woman in good physical condition can experience full arousal and orgasm—and both men and women have reported the experience.

Let me state the obvious: You can't be concentrating on a sex fantasy and reading this book at the same time. Ideally, you should memorize these six steps. You can also write them down on a card—just a word or two for each step—and refer to them if necessary. First, read through all the steps.

1. *Get nude in comfortable surroundings.*

You don't want to be disturbed by phones, visitors, chills, sweating, or bright lights. You want a comfortable chair in a comfortable room, and most people want quiet. Be sure you're able to relax—*really* relax.

2. *Breathe erotically.*

Just to show you how important proper breathing is, try this experiment now. Breathe as you do when you are asleep. Some of you are probably thinking, "I don't know how I breathe when I'm asleep—I'm asleep!" True enough. But you do know how others breathe while sleeping—a quick inhale, and a long, slow exhale. Something like, "Ah *soooo*, ah *soooo*." Try to do that now, a quick, shallow in-breath followed by a long exhale. If you continue that for as few as 20 seconds, you'll actually feel your body relax. You'll grow sleepy. In fact, on restless nights I can usually help myself to fall asleep in just a few minutes by forcing myself into a sleep breathing pattern. Sleep breathing works because it creates a minor oxygen deficit in the brain, which has a tranquilizing effect.

We also have an alertness pattern of breathing. It begins with a long inhale followed by a short exhale. The goal is to keep the lungs filled with fresh oxygen, which is carried by the blood to the brain, encouraging alertness. This is the sort of breathing you want to do during the first few minutes after relaxation and continue until you reach step five. At that point, you actually want to begin panting or gasping for breath. That's our natural method of breathing when we are either fighting, fleeing or copulating. It triggers the neurochemical responses that bring about heightened sexual arousal and orgasm.

3. *Focus on your fantasy*.

I believe that many of us, especially those who are creative, can be erotically stimulated by a variety of scenarios, including most of those described in this book. Others might have only a handful of situations that turn on their erector sets. My guess is that, for virtually all of us, there's that one red-hot fantasy that's anchored in the core of who we are. Perhaps, in a way that we can't even understand, it's rooted in our childhood or early adolescence. Right now we're not interested in why it has such a hold on us, only what it is that has that hold. That's the scene—the fantasy—that you want to discover.

Begin putting it together. Set the stage. Bring the performers out of the wings. Let the action begin. But don't allow things to get too heavy yet. First, we need to make the fantasy more vivid.

4. *Intensify the sensory input*.

Here's where we begin to move into superfantasies. We do that, first, by intensifying the sensory detail of our fantasies.

What do you *see*? Skin, certainly—but look more closely. Study the pores. Is there hair? Is it straight, curly, peach fuzz? What color is it? Are there organs in the picture? Examine them closely, every aspect of them. Make the vision in your mind clear, focused—real.

What do you *hear*? Even if you're watching a man or woman masturbate, there are slurping sounds, breathing, moans. Perhaps the springs of a bed are squeaking. Perhaps the window is open and traffic is passing by. Listen carefully. Make the sounds real.

What do you *smell*? Is the woman wearing perfume, the man cologne? Do body smells turn you on? The sweat smells differently in the armpit than it does at the scrotum. Perhaps you smell the fragrance of a lubricant or other odors that appeal to you. Concentrate on them. Make them real.

Have you *tasted* the body or bodies in your fantasy? As I write this, I can taste the salt along the ribcage, the tanginess of body fluids. Think about what you're doing in your imagination. Make the tastes real.

What do you *feel*? Hold a breast in your hand. Weigh it. Shape it into your palm. Feel the testicles within the scrotum, the hairs against the palm of your hand. Brush your cheek against the pubic area. Does the hair scratch or caress your face? Touch the body, play with it. Hold the buttocks in both hands. Gently rub the backs of your fingers across the face. There's so much to touch. Feel it—*really* feel it.

5. *Intensify the feelings in your body.*

You are part of your fantasy, and your body is feeling all sorts of things. Has your breathing increased to short, rapid gasps: A hollowness seems to develop in the pit of your stomach. You feel your face flushing with the increased blood as your heart begins to pound. Hands are touching you—or organs. Mouths are on your body, at your nipples and genitals, perhaps your toes and fingers. Allow these feelings to surge through you. Allow them to become real.

6. *Believe That It's Happening Now.*

Here's the key. It's possible to literally *experience* being fellated, feeling a mouth slide back and forth along your penis. It's possible to *feel* the penetration of the phallus as it impales you. I don't mean as you *imagine* this happening, except in the most literal sense. I mean the sensation is as real as sensations can be. As it becomes utterly real in this precise minute, the natural result is orgasm.

When I first wrote about the psychic orgasm, a few readers wrote expressing disappointment that, although they tingled throughout their bodies with a new sense of eroticism while pursuing the ultimate fantasy, they were still unable to achieve the psychic orgasm. Why aren't they getting there, I pondered. Then, after rereading many of the letters, I think I found the answer.

The fantasy must cease to be a fantasy and become reality. I used the term *absorbed*. I might have said totally permeated by the truth of the *reality* in your head. Here's the difference between that and an ordinary fantasy. I might sit back and imagine someone fellating me. I might see his or her head moving up and down as the lips caress my shaft. I might smell the perfume or cologne. I might hear the slurping sounds, and my own moans. I might even run my fingers through the hair. True, few ordinary fantasies become so detailed. Still, it's nothing more than a vividly imagined fantasy. But there is yet another step possible. That fantasy can suddenly become reality. That's what real autosuggetion is about. I begin to actually *feel* the lips or the hand moving back and forth—I can feel the *pressure* of the lips or the hand. *I am actually being fellated or masturbated.* It is simply a matter of relaxing and enjoying while I build to the inevitable climax.

And it *is* inevitable. Once I can feel the contact, once I know that I am really being brought to orgasm, that it is *inevitable*, there is nothing for it but to spill over the brink. The slightest distraction can bring you back to ground zero—even posing the question to yourself as you feel the orgasm approach, "Is this really going to happen all the way?" *Of course* it's going to happen—it can't *not* happen. It is *inevitable*.

Of course we know that not all people are alike—some are particularly susceptible to suggestion; others are incapable of it. Most of us are probably in between—capable under ideal circumstances. It's not something you need to do—the Boy Scouts don't offer merit badges in psychic orgasms; the psychic orgasm is no more intense than orgasms achieved through ordinary means. It's in the same category as autofellatio. If you can do it, fine. If not, join the masses. That doesn't detract from your sexual pleasures one iota.

ALTERNATE APPROACHES TO INTENSIFYING FANTASY

The True Experience

Forty years have passed since, at age 15, in the basement of my home, my brother, my cousin and a friend, all about 13 and 14, began discussing erections with me. I don't know if they were in collusion or not, but they asked me what my penis looked like when it got hard. So, being of a bashful disposition, I stripped nude including the removal of my shoes and socks, stretched out on a table and told the friend, who seemed most interested, that he could pump it up for me if he liked. It turns out, he liked indeed. That promptly led to an erection the likes of which these youngsters had never seen, since I was a year or two older than they. There were ohs and ahs and gasps of disbelief, which filled me with narcissistic sexual power and led to prompt ejaculation.

I have relived that true experience literally hundreds of times through the years, and it remains as erotic a daydream as any I have known. If you have difficulty creating an intense original fantasy, you might try recalling a really, really hot experience in real life. Perhaps it involves others as mine does, or it could be a naked walk in the woods, driving your car nude at night—or in the daytime. It could be peering through some-one's window—accidentally, of course—and seeing something forbidden. Whatever it is, see if you can recreate every aspect of that intense experience, using all five senses.

Draw or Write Your Fantasy

History has known some very well paid pornographers, from Henry Miller and Anais Nin to John Preston and Aubrey Beardsley, but no successful pornographer ever wrote or paint-ed simply for money. They wrote or painted with one hand while using the other to caress what Mark Twain called the "Mammoth cod" or female equivalent. Writing or drawing your sexual fantasies has the added bonus of imposing restraint. The lust level builds as the creative process proceeds. Ultimately, there's an almost overwhelming hunger to put the creative process aside and get on with celebrating the self. But no, one must deny the hunger, and the more it's denied as one's thoughts are engaged in the details of the sexual act, the greater the desire becomes.

Actually, teenage boys do this all the time, and I suspect teenage girls do as well—although I've not talked to teenaged girls about such things. As an adolescent male, I might doodle the letter B in my history notebook, having no idea why I drew a B rather than an L or X. Immediately I realize B stands for boobs, and furthermore, if I were to hang from the ceiling above Madeline Lemonjello, I would gaze down upon the largest boobs in all of Irvington High School, and, from my position, I might even be able to see her nipples, because she always wore such low-cut blouses just to tease the boys.

I would draw the nipples on the B, then her waist and spread legs, and then of course a penis lying on its side so that it was actually my dick at the entrance of Madeline Lemonjello's honey pot, and then...

I've sold many erotic short stories over the years. Usually, they started out as old fashioned heterosexual encounters, the creation of which led not only to a pay check but a few orgies with myself. And, since I made a living writing, I often asked my typist to change the gender of one of the lead characters, along with her name—say, from Barbara to Bill, and switch a few genital organs. I'd then sell exactly the same story under a different name to an obviously non-competing magazine. Reading the new version led to another series of orgasms. Jimmy Stewart was right: It really is a wonderful life. Imagine being paid for putting your sexual fantasies on paper.

Whether you're drawing, painting, or writing your fantasies, here's this added bonus: A month from now you may pull out the material you've created today and discover it will trigger a fresh new response. Eventually, you might have an entire volume of material created uniquely for you, appealing to your own favorite inspirations. As the years go by, you will find in it a special joy.

Explore the Forbidden

Setting out to improve your sex life through fantasy, don't be afraid to explore the forbidden. Now, when I say that, I'm assuming that you know the difference between reality and fantasy. You know that the world is your oyster when it comes to your imagination, but in reality you have no right putting your desires ahead of another person's well-being. I have no patience with the individual who thinks he can use or abuse people sexually. That's not what sex—or maturity, for that matter—is about. Do whatever you like in your head—just keep it there.

That being said, why not explore in fantasy those aspects of sexuality that have frightened you? Have you avoided thinking about homosexuality? Are you afraid of what you will discover? What about sadomasochism, exhibitionism?

Think of human sexuality as a vast, undulating prairie. You can run free anywhere across that terrain. It's all yours for the taking, in your imagination. There are joys out there that you may not even imagine. Set yourself free to explore. And expect over the course of your lifetime not to be sexually static. Your interests will move like the breeze through the wheat on those plains. Today you will fantasize in this direction, tomorrow in that. Perhaps you'll settle down after a decade or two, concentrating in one area of fantasy. Or you may not, preferring instead to drift in and out of interests and orientations, as restless as the wind. That is your legacy as a human being, as a creature with imagination, capable of sexual fantasy.

CHAPTER XII

Pornography as Fantasy

"Pornography," Says Robert Stoller, M.D., "is the communicated sexual fantasy of a dynamically related group of people."[1]

Pornography: Untold millennia ago, a man stood at the wall of a cave, and drew with a chunk of clay or charcoal the act which the night before had made him ecstatically happy. He and his fellow humans freely sketched pictures of penises and vaginas, of copulating humans and animals. Others observed these drawings and were inspired to go and do likewise. There were no censors then—in fact, quite the contrary. In many societies, genitals were objects of worship. In others, copulation was a sacrament, similar to communion. The ecstasy of orgasm was as close to a transcendent spiritual experience as humans could know. Portraying that experience in art was the equivalent of today's crucifix and stained glass church windows. They were sacred sexual icons. Even now, carved in stone or painted on the walls of buildings, they are found in Greece, Italy, Japan, Ireland, Britain, India and countless other nations.

These depictions were sacred celebrations of sexuality. They were also often pornography, which means writing by or about prostitutes. In ancient times, a great deal of sexual activity did indeed involve prostitutes—youths and adults, both male and female, who were church fund-raisers, having sex for money which they turned over to temple priests. Prostitution, sexually explicit pictures and writing, along with nudity and even public masturbation, became moral issues only when new religions—among them Christianity and Islamism—declared war on sex. (I've discussed the reasons for this in *More Joy....*)

Today, what I prefer to call sexually explicit material, since most of it does not involve prostitutes and the term pornography has a negative connotation, is as popular as ever. Think of it: Long before any currently popular religion existed, primitive humans entertained themselves depicting erotic scenarios, and now, at the dawn of the 21st centruy, we continue to pursue this fundamental pleasure. If anything is "natural" to our species, it's the creation and appreciation of hard-core erotica.

And it's a virtually universal pleasure. More than 25,000 retail outlets in the U. S. carry adult video cassettes. That doesn't include dozens of small boutiques and large mail order companies that deal directly with the customer. During 1996 in the United States, stores reported a total of 665 million rentals of adult tapes. At a minimum, erotic entertainment is an eight-billion-dollar-a-year business.

The adult entertainment industry is responsible for many thousands of full-time jobs, most of them in manufacturing, distribution, and sales. Each year, one in four Americans buys or rents an erotic film. That doesn't include magazines and books, and it doesn't tell us how many others bought similar merchandise in previous years.[2] It's my guess that 85 percent of American households contain sexually explicit magazines, books, videos—or all three.

And what about the other 15 percent? I'll tell you a story about some of them. Years ago, I worked for a publishing company outside of New York City. I had to travel to the Big Apple regularly on business, and, because I was considered sexually uninhibited, I was asked by four fellow editors to buy an x-rated film from time to time. They actually chipped in to purchase the film—all I had to do was go into the store and buy it, which they were reluctant to do. I scheduled a viewing. The editors each made up their excuses to their wives and came to my home. I showed the film, they went their separate ways, and I kept the flick. Actually, I had no choice. None of them would even consider having an x-rated film in his house.

Personally, I have never met a man who has not seen a sexually explicit film or read an erotic passage. I'm sure such a person exists, but he must be a particularly peculiar individual, differing as he does so radically from the mainstream.

A study of 2,250 18- to 74-year-old men showed that sex is more fun for those who enjoy sexually explicit material. These men also tend to have no discernible sexual hang-ups or negative religious influences. They start having sex early, and think sex is important.[3]

Sexually explicit material serves one primary function — it helps us to feel lust, or sexual desire. When a man is unable to get an erection, he may go to his physician and get a prescription for Viagra, MUSE, or similar medication, and almost immediately it's party time. To my knowledge, no right-wing crusade against the immorality of Viagra has taken form. But perhaps this individual doesn't need the drugs at all. Perhaps all he needs is to have his libido sufficiently stimulated to produce the erection he needs. In such cases, "pornography" can be the therapy of choice.

Let me give you the most common scenario with which I'm familiar. A man reaches his early fifties. He has been relatively faithful to his wife of 30 years, sating his sexual drive copulating with her 2.5 times per week (don't ask me how he achieves the .5—the statistics come from medical research), and masturbating to fantasies perhaps twice more each week. But in his early fifties, his sex drive begins to wane. Neither his wife's body nor his fantasies inspire him as they once did.

Even if he were to turn to potency-inducing drugs, he might well develop an erection with no clear passion for what to do with it. At first, of course, the erection itself would function as an aphrodisiac. His own potency would inspire him. But that, too, would cease to move him soon enough. What he needs is something new that could reach inside and crank up the libido, the lust level.

What many men do is to find a new sexual partner, often someone much younger and more enthusiastic sexually. But that same need can be met by erotica, if fantasy itself is no longer effective, and, inspired by that erotica, the man may suddenly discover his wife to be much more desirable than he had remembered.

The same can be true of *women* who lack sexual desire. I've already quoted Joseph LoPiccolo, Ph.D., who tells of a woman patient who had never reached orgasm.

LoPiccolo instructed her to masturbate using a vibrator, lubricant jelly, and sexually explicit materials. Finally, after three weeks of 45-minute sessions, she reached orgasm.[4]

Just as the fantasies in your head can have a healing effect, so can erotica. Writing specifically about sadistic fantasies, Walter Braun, M.D., says, "Such masturbation fantasies are safety-valves. Masturbation in these cases may be compared to a lightning conductor that diverts the potential explosive danger of perverted fantasy away from society and buries it in the hidden depths of the masturbator's soul." [5]

Braun says that some people are not endowed with a sufficiently vivid imagination to create their own fantasies, which leaves them with two alternatives: Either they act out in the real world the behavior that turns them on, or they find "an acceptable substitute. Such collections, for example, comprising pictures showing situations dear to the owner's libido, are known as 'Satan's bibles.' The illustrations are very seldom made to order. They are usually clippings from magazines, accumulated with infinite patience and pasted into an album, sort of a scrapbook." In other words, these people create their own erotica. Dr. Braun quotes Dr. Wilhelm Stekel, in *Sexual Aberrations:*

> He once knew a policeman who showed him a very elegantly bound album of magazine clippings that the man had altered by drawing obscene figures on them and adding grotesque sexual organs. In a handwritten story accompanying the illustrations, the 35-year-old policeman described how he tortured and raped these fantasy women. Scenes of sexual assault and torments occurred time and again in a way that clearly showed how the man's imagination worked. Stekel referred to this sort of painstaking composition as 'the bible' of the sado-masachist. The amazing thing is that in real life

this sexually obsessed guardian of public moral-
ity was a shy, weak, even impotent human being,
who in all his life—even after he married—had
never successfully engaged in sexual intercourse. Nor had he ever molested anybody.
Giving written and pictorial form to his fantasies
in his 'bible' was his only way of approximating
to sexual satisfaction.

Braun himself tells of a man, a young army officer, who
came to him emotionally distraught:

> After a few sessions in my consulting
> room he told me of his sadomasochistic inter-
> ests. He was fascinated by phantasies of corset-
> ed women, who were bound, raped, flogged and
> tortured. At the same time these phantasies dis-
> gusted him, and he told me tearfully that he
> would never think of actually doing horrible
> things like that to women, and had ultimately
> come to me because he dreaded that one day he
> would forget himself and commit one of these
> sex-crimes he so often dreamed of. I told him
> that merely repressing his phantasies would not
> solve anything.
>
> "But I'm so ashamed of all these dis-
> graceful ideas!" he said.
>
> At a subsequent session he revealed to
> me that, some months before, he had taken what
> was to him a very drastic decision. Until then he
> had kept his own "Satan's bible": in that book he
> had amassed pictures of corseted women that he
> found in women's magazines, fashion cata-
> logues and so on. With pen and ink he used to

adapt those illustrations to his requirements. He was very pleased with his collection and would pour over it for hours in rapture.

"What happened to it?" I asked.

He shrugged his shoulders. "I destroyed it... I destroyed all traces of it... Sometimes I am sorry I took that decision, but on soberer reflection I know it was a wise thing to do...."

"But what made you do that?"

Again he shrugged his shoulders and looked a little embarrassed. "I started to think about myself and about what I was doing in compiling that collection. It struck me as a very childish thing indeed—imagine! A grown-up man carefully cutting out pictures and touching them up in ink and sticking them in a book! I mean to say...I *had* to put a stop to it, didn't I?"

"Why?"

"Well, because...because I couldn't go on. It doesn't make sense. I'm twenty-eight now, I'm no longer a child...I don't need a collection like that any more to keep me happy...."

"Are you quite sure about that?"

He didn't answer.

I told A.M. that he probably *did* need that album and that it represented to him a harmless compensation for all those things he would like to do but which could never happen in reality. I warned him that he might only succeed in turning himself into a very unsettled, neurotic and morose person, and the long term effects of that might be unpredictable but scarcely encouraging.

"But common sense...," he began.

I told him that in cases like his it wasn't wise to follow the dictates of common sense if these imposed inhibitions that could bring worse consequences in their train. In dealing with people's imaginations it is not easy to say what is childish and what is sensible and so on. I wonder how many sexual offenders have committed their crimes after having tried to do what common sense demanded. It may well be that A.M. still sometimes feels childish, or ashamed of himself, but I am quite sure he is not going to give vent to any act of sadism, for he has his safety-valve once more.[7]

Opposition to pornography

Those who oppose pornography do so for a number of reasons. One is that it might actually encourage the committing of sex crimes. This is another example of those many sexual myths dearly held by perhaps millions of people for which there is *absolutely no evidence*. In fact, evidence suggests the opposite, just as it does for fantasies. F. M. Christensen argues that "the Williams Committee, which studied the pornography issue for the British government, reported it was unable to uncover any cases of a probable link between pornography and violent sex crimes. Instead, the committee remarked, 'One can study case after case of sex crimes and murder without finding any hint at all that pornography was present in the background.' A similar conclusion was drawn earlier by researchers who surveyed juvenile criminal cases in the United States."[8]

When Denmark legalized all sorts of pornography in the 1960's, there was absolutely no increase in any type of sex crime—and voyeurism dropped by 80 percent and child sex abuse by about 70 percent. In fact, as I've already argued, Christensen says, "many psychiatrists who have worked with sexually disturbed patients believe that pornography often has the effect of preventing sexual violence. Many sex offenders themselves report that this is the case, moreover. Dr. John Money, who deals with sex offenders in his clinic, reports that offenders commonly disclose in the course of counseling therapy that pornography helps them contain their abnormal sexuality within imagination only, as a fantasy.'"

Those seeking evidence closer to home need look no farther than Cincinnati, Ohio. A survey published in 1996 in the *Journal of Psychology & Human Sexuality* concluded that "statistical data do not confirm the hypothesis that decreased pornography consumption leads to decrease in rape rates."

Cincinnati must be one of the most boring cities on earth—it has no peep shows, adult bookstores, bars with nude dancing, escort services, massage parlors, no adult video stores or sexually explicit magazines. Authorities outlawed everything sexual because they said that "pornography" led to rape and (there they go again) child sexual abuse.

The researchers found no such thing. There was *no* decrease in rape or child sexual abuse, in spite of these draconian efforts.

But shouldn't kids, at least, be protected from pornography? The Internet is bringing this conflict to a head. Allowed free access to library computers, your children, properly motivated and with the necessary access information, can see and learn all sorts of things about the human body and its sexuality. And there's the rub, if you will pardon the expression.

Mark Y. Herring, of Oklahoma Baptist University, writes in the May 1, 1998, issue of *Library Journal*, "If a great work can inspire courage, greatness and magnanimity, then bad ones can also provoke lust, rage, and parvanimity...."

Another librarian writes in that same issue, "We don't put snuff films in the video section of the library." Then she makes her point: "Why allow material offensive to the reasonable and rational person into the library just because it comes on the Internet?"

Cheryl Banick's question, in effect, is "Why *should* anyone of any age have access to sex information just because they want to?" *My* question is, "Why *shouldn't* they?"

I was a kid once, as interested in sex as anyone else my age—which is to say, not very. I remember that Michael Lowenthall and I met behind his sofa when we were six years old and rubbed our penises together. At the time I felt heat flashes that virtually took my breath away. But you know something? We soon grew tired of that and never bothered doing it again. We had other things to do. We climbed fences, chased each other across Newark's garage roofs, ran through people's gardens, explored the neighborhood.

Four or five years later, I discovered my father's treasure trove of pornography. These were photos, many of them taken by him, mostly of my mother and he, in some cases the two of them together in sexual acts. Then, again, I felt the flush, the breathlessness. I'm sure I sprouted an erection, but I knew nothing of masturbation.

Those photos remained in that same cabinet even after I left for college at age 18, but I perused them only twice more, briefly, curious about the secret play my parents were involved in; also, even more, the strange things that I felt in my body at observing them. But I wasn't yet ready for sex, and soon became caught up in other matters. I was, in a sense, educating myself in ideal fashion, sating my curiosity.

What's wrong with young people sating their curiosity about sex? How dare any educated person equate that to a *snuff* film in which someone is murdered?

Here's the line in the sand. Is sex—the knowledge, portrayal and practice of it—good, positive, and celebrative? Or is it to be equated with "rage, and parvanimity," with "snuff films" and that which is "offensive to the reasonable and rational person?" Ultimately, we are not only defending the First Amendment, but the rightness and naturalness of the body and its sexuality, and, the healthful, happy, celebrative depictions of that sexuality in every medium.

Can pornography ever be harmful and lead you to sex crimes? For anyone genuinely interested in the facts, the information is available in not one but two federally funded investigations into the subject by the U.S. government. Pornography appears to have no—no—negative effects on society. Today, you're unlikely to hear a knowledgeable person argue against pornography because it incites people to act on what they see and read. Instead, through efforts by feminists Catharine A. MacKinnon and Andrea Dworkin, the definition of pornography has been rewritten by officials in the city of Minneapolis, the nation of Canada, and elsewhere as follows: "Pornography is defined as the graphic, sexually explicit subordination of women whether in pictures or in words that also includes one or more of the following: where women are presented dehumanized as sexual objects, things, or commodities; where women are presented as sexual objects to enjoy pain or humiliation; where women are presented as sexual objects who experience sexual pleasure in being raped; where women are presented as sexual objects tied up or cut up or mutilated or bruised or physically hurt; where women are presented in postures of sexual submission; where women's body parts are exhibited, such that women are reduced to those parts; where women are being presented being penetrated by objects or animals; where women are presented in scenarios of degradation, injury, abasement, torture, shown as filthy or inferior, bleeding, bruised, or hurt in a context of these conditions sexually."[9]

In the United States, this definition of pornography has rightly been ruled unconstitutional—it discriminates against *men*. Under the law, it's perfectly acceptable to strip a man naked in a video, kick him in the testicles, force him to suck a penis while being impaled by another, eject semen in his face and then beat the shit out of him—but if he's a she, the whole thing is suddenly pornographic. (This truly screwball definition of pornography is still being enforced in Canada, incidentally.)

Beyond the bias against males, that definition of pornography also wipes out virtually every sex fantasy ever entertained by either a man or a woman. In our sick compulsion to put a sexually sterile spin on life, we go to the extreme of denying some quite obvious things about human sexuality. The truth is that we are *all* sex objects. When it comes to sex—which is not the same as our everyday relationships with men and women—we don't fantasize about a woman's collarbone or nostril or big toe (there are always exceptions), but about her breasts, her buttocks, her legs, her abdomen, her lips, her vagina. We fixate on his testicles, penis, chest, abdomen, lips. There are certain parts of the body—and if you wish to call those parts "objects," so be it—that we find erotic. Those are the "parts" we play with in bed if we are fortunate enough to have a partner. Those are the parts we fantasize about when we are not so fortunate, or when we prefer sex with ourselves. Those are the parts that we like to look at or think about or read about when we seek to be turned on by sexually explicit material.

Personally, I'm delighted to report that I've been a sex object since the age of thirteen, and one of my few dreads in life is that I might live to an age when I will no longer be a sex object. Play with any part of me you like—I will be grateful for the attention, aware that any "object" is a part of the whole.

Incidentally, millions of women oppose the Dworkin-MacKinnon definition of pornography in that the subjugation that the two oppose has nothing to do with typical sexually explicit videos. Just as S&M constitutes only one of many fantasizes that we entertain, so S&M videos are not disproportionately represented in the erotic video marketplace. (Violent S&M videos are rare.)

In Fact, feminists as a whole denouce the Dworkin-MacKinnon stand on pornography for another reason as well: Religious fundamentalists have rallied behind it. Understand what this means. Religious extremists so hate sexually explicit material that they embrace two women who support abortion and deny the inerrancy of the Bible. Personally, I don't blame Dworkin and MacKinnon for "going after the money," any more than I blame Little Richard who, with his career floundering, got saved, then took his gig to the sawdust trail, only to abandon the calling when his career as a rock star revived.

The real reason pornography is attacked in our society is because of the conflict that is almost two millennia old: our natural tendency to celebrate our sexuality and consider it something sacred as opposed to evangelical religions with competing symbols of the sacred. We read in Matthew, Chapter 5, verse 28, "But I say unto you that whosoever looketh on a woman to lust after her hath committed adultery with her already in his heart." It's been argued that pornography is effective precisely because we lust after one or more of the "sex objects" being portrayed in the writing, painting, or photos.

Therefore, pornography is indirectly condemned by the teachings of Jesus, at least according to this passage.

But it is the hypocrite, not the adulterer in his heart, that Jesus condemns to hell. In fact, Jesus nowhere in the scriptures attacks a single sexual offense, not even when he speaks to the woman caught in adultery. Because of his wisdom, her life was spared.

We all fall short of most of the standards set in the Bible. Yet, considering the frequency with which the "looketh upon a woman to lust after her" business is quoted, you'd think these were the only words Jesus ever spoke.

Most of the writers of the Bible, from Moses on, competed for adherents with religions that openly celebrated human sexuality, even to the extent of having public orgies. That created an anti-sexual backlash which culminated in the writings of St. Paul, born and raised in the Greek pagan city of Tarsus. Under the circumstances, it's remarkable that Jesus never expressed sex negativism.

What is the role of pornography in an ideal society? I'll let B.D. of Arlington, Virginia, answer that question in his own words:

> In spite of growing up in a conservative New England town, there were two newsstands that sold girlie magazines. I soon discovered that looking at these magazines gave me a hard-on and made me want to masturbate. I soon began to buy magazines like *Eyeful, Titter, Beauty Parade* and other similar magazines, all of which featured scantily clad models. Knowing that if I got caught by my father with this kind of magazine I would be in big trouble, I hid them where they would not be found but readily available when I

wanted to masturbate. Looking at the pictures, very tame when compared with today's magazines, allowed me to fantasize, enhancing the pleasure of my masturbation.

Not long after I began buying these girlie magazines, I found that the other newsstand began to sell art photography magazines which featured a section on nude models. While they were nude, the genital areas were either covered or airbrushed out. Still, it gave me new things to fantasize about. I was seeing bare breasts for the first time. I began to masturbate more and to enjoy it more with my new-found treasures.

In buying these art photography magazines I befriended one of the clerks in the newsstand who was to become my first steady source of pornography and masturbation material. I remember being in the newsstand one Sunday afternoon to see if there were any new magazines. It was just before closing time. My clerk friend asked me to wait for him to close the store, that he had something to show me. After he locked up he took me into the stock room and, after obtaining a promise that I would never tell where I got what he was going to show me, he handed me a stack of *Modern Sunbathing* magazines, one of the nudist magazines of the time. Again, making me promise I would never reveal where I got them if I ever got caught with them, he told me to pick up what I wanted. I picked out what I could afford and asked him if he would save the rest for me, which he agreed to do, and told me that from time to time he would have some other interesting things. While he never asked what I did with them, you know he knew I was masturbating while looking at the pictures. True to his promise, he did have interesting things for me from time to time.

Up to this time I had no pictures or magazines which showed the pubic area of either men or women. *Modern Sunbathing*, like the art photography magazines, were retouched. One night I stopped in to see my friend to ask if he had any new nudist magazines. He told me to come back in about a half hour. I found something to do to pass the time and when I went back and asked him again, he said, "How would you like some photos of twat?" With that I about came in my pants and didn't really have an answer, but just kind of shook my head up and down. He handed me something that looked like a deck of playing cards and that was exactly what it was, a French Deck. In his funny way he asked me if I liked the pictures. I was still speechless, but I'm sure I must have been grinning from ear to ear. These were the first pictures I had ever seen in which couples were fucking, sucking, eating pussy and in a couple of the photos the woman was taking it up her rear. You can bet that I never made it through the whole deck, 52 cards plus 2 jokers, before I came. For the rest of my high school years my friend kept me well supplied with the latest (for those days) in pornography.

It was during these days in high school, being taught that masturbation was wrong and sinful, that I would have my guilt feelings about my masturbation and pornography. After masturbating I would make a promise to myself never to masturbate again and more often than not, I burned all my pornography. Two days later I would be back visiting my friend and asking what new things he had for me and would again be enjoying the pleasures of masturbation. This was about the time I began to realize that masturbation is a natural thing, just like having a wet dream, that I was not alone or different and there was really nothing wrong with it. Once I got to that point, I got over my guilt trips and really began to enjoy it.

In all the years I have been collecting pornography and masturbating, never once have I ever had the thought or desire to rape anyone or sexually molest a child. I find it very difficult to understand how masturbation and pornography can be seen as the cause of violence. I would say that masturbation and pornography are a sexual outlet and therefore are deterrents to violence, rape and child molesting, rather than a cause.

While I am a heterosexual, I do have a few solo male masturbation videos in my collection. I enjoy watching videos of other guys masturbating. I also have begun a collection recently of photos of guys with huge penises. After viewing them I can honestly say, under the right circumstances and with the right person (he'd have to have a mega penis), I believe I would consent to mutual masturbation. I think I would enjoy holding one of those big penises in my hand and feel it grow big and hard while I stroked it until it ejaculated. I also have been turned on by the sight of big, uncircumcised penises.

I love looking at photos of big tits and pink pussy and/or watching a video of someone like Melissa Mounds, Busty Belle, Beverlee Hills, Susie Sparks, or L. A. Bust fondling their big boobs, tweaking their nipples, or diddling their twats as I masturbate. It provides the visual picture to enhance the fantasy. Seldom does a day go by that I do not look at some kind of pornography. While I don't masturbate every time I do look at it, it keeps the thought and the desire to masturbate in my mind. My favorite pornography features models with mega breasts and in particular, pregnant and lactating models.

To somewhat establish my credibility, I am a college graduate and have a Master's Degree. I have retired from two careers and now provide consulting service on a part-time basis. I have been happily married for 30 years, raised four children, put them all through college and all are now in professional careers. I would hope that that would quiet all those who say masturbation is the root of all evil and will make you crazy.

Pornography and the Law

The word pornography, as I've said, is from two Greek

sources meaning prostitute and I write—literally writings by or about prostitutes. Today, various dictionaries describe it as writing or other art designed specifically and exclusively to titillate sexually or, as in the Hammond International Dictionary, "Obscene literature or art."

At least in the legal sense, that definition is as far from correct as can be—and that makes all the difference. Pornography is not illegal. Obscenity is. The difference has been carefully spelled out by the Supreme Court, which makes it the final word.

Here's when a piece of pornography (sexually explicit and even titillating) becomes obscene:

1. When *taken as a whole*, it appeals to prurient, or lustful interest. (Of course it seems the height of absurdity that something could be ruled illegal simply because it turns us on sexually. Why on earth should it be a crime to be turned on sexually? What's wrong with sex?)

2. Whether the work depicts or describes in a patently offensive way sexual conduct specifically defined by the applicable state law. (It doesn't count if you are patently offended by vivid descriptions of murder and torture or injustice; they're not obscene, but perfectly legal.)

3. Whether the work, *taken as a whole,* lacks serious literary, artistic, political, or scientific value.

Now here's the good part: Contemporary *community* standards are no longer sufficient to satisfy this last requirement. Whether or not a work has literary, educational, spiritual or political value must now be judged, according to the U. S. Supreme Court, by *national* standards. As a practical example, this book cannot legally be judged by the standards of New York City. The standards of you, its readers across the nation, must be considered.[10]

You *Can* Go to Jail for What You're Thinking

This book is about sexual fantasy, and so it's appropriate to end this chapter with discussion of a criminal prosecution in which a man was sent to prison for possessing child pornography—not because the film itself contained even one pornographic element, but because of the *fantasies* the jury assumed the man was having while watching the innocuous video.

In 1991, police raided the apartment of Stephen A. Knox of State College, Pennsylvania. The authorities found three videocassettes produced by the Las Vegas-based Nather Company. Knox, then an honors graduate student at Pennsylvania State University and working on a doctorate in history, was charged and quickly convicted of receiving through the mail and possessing visual depictions of minors engaged in "sexually explicit conduct." This was Knox's second conviction for receiving child pornography through the mail. (The company which produced and sold these videos, incidentally, was never charged.)

Exactly what were these pornographic videos all about? They showed girls, aged ten to seventeen, dressed in bathing suits, leotards, and underwear—similar to the depictions you see in Sears, K-Mart's and Wal-Mart's ads in your Sunday newspapers each week. The girls posed awkwardly and danced around. The camera zoomed in and lingered on their midsections, although at no time was any shape or outline of genitalia recognizable. Knox was found guilty of possessing films that included scenes of "lascivious exhibition of the genitals or pubic area of any person."

The conviction was upheld in the Third U.S. Circuit Court of Appeals.

Knox appealed to the U.S. Supreme Court. Solicitor General Drew Days of the Justice Department filed a brief in the case arguing that the Appeals Court had "utilized an impermissibly broad standard" for determining what was child pornography. Most people, including the Solicitor General, have a pretty clear idea of what child pornography is—and it doesn't include depictions of clothed children romping on a beach, whether or not the camera is focused on midsections. Days urged the justices of the highest court in the land to send the case back to the Philadelphia-based Third U.S. Circuit Court of Appeals for further study.

Suddenly the Clinton Administration, via its Justice Department, became a sitting duck for politicians seeking the conservative vote. In November of 1993, all 100 Senators and an overwhelming majority of Representatives voted in favor of a non-binding resolutions attacking the Justice Department's "narrow view of the law," stating that it did not accurately reflect the intent of Congress in drawing up anti-child pornography legislation. President Bill Clinton, sensing the potential for political damage, responded, "I fully agree with the Senate about what the proper scope of the child pornography law should be. I find all forms of child pornography offensive and harmful, as I know you do." He publicly rebuked Attorney General Janet Reno and made it clear that he wanted his administration "to lead aggressively in the attack against the scourge of child pornography."

But by then, the Supreme Court of the United States had already ruled, persuaded by Solicitor General Days' argument that "the court erred in holding that simply focusing on the midsection of a clothed body may constitute an 'exhibition' of the unrevealed body parts beneath the garments." Days argued that the law required that the genitals or pubic area, though covered, be at least discernible, and that the child be "lasciviously engaging in sexual conduct." (As one of Knox's lawyers said, "This material simply isn't child pornography. It's crazy to litigate extreme cases like this.")

On November 1, the Supreme Court sent the case back to the Philadelphia court for re-examination in light of the Justice Department's arguments.

Almost overnight, the Third Circuit Court again found Knox guilty, concluding that neither nudity nor any discernibility of the genitals is necessary for a child pornography conviction. The Justice Department, inundated by protest letters for its previous stance, did an about-face and supported the Knox conviction. Knox again appealed to the Supreme Court. The Court refused, without comment, to review the case. Knox went to prison to serve his five-year sentence.

Let me make some concessions here. It seems obvious, based on the previous conviction for possessing child pornography, that Knox was a pedophile. Fantasies and depictions of naked children, and possibly naked children engaged in sex, got his juices flowing. Let's also assume, for argument's sake, that he bought the three videos of the girls cavorting in various positions because he thought they would be sexually stimulating. Beyond that, we may assume nothing.

But the courts *did* in fact make a catastrophically important assumption. They assumed that they could read the mind of Stephen Knox. They *assumed* that these videos *did* turn him on, stimulate him sexually, and as such they were pornographic. Note that the films, objectively, were *not* pornographic. Shown at a conference on children at play, no one would have thought them pornographic for a second. Found in a collection of videos at your house or mine, no district attorney would have given them a second thought. Even Stephen Knox himself may have bought those videos only to be disappointed to find that he had no erotic interest in them. But the courts! They read the mind of Stephen Knox and *knew* that for him these mundane depictions opened the door to perverse fantasies, and these *assumed fantasies* in Stephen Knox's mind made those videos obscene and their possession illegal.

I abhor child sexual abuse. I'm convinced on good evidence that children who are used to make pornographic films and photos are severely traumatized in many cases by the process. Often they're literally forced to participate and are punished if they don't perform properly. There should be no tolerance for such activities. *But we cannot prosecute people and throw them in prison for what we assume is going on in their heads.*

A man is serving a five-year sentence not because of what he was *viewing* but what he was *thinking.* You might never have thought you would have to take a public stand on the right to fantasize, but such a day might actually come. Your erotic fantasies are a pathway to unbridled pleasure. They may open the door to healing, and some men and women have found spiritual solace in their sexual fantasies. Above all, your fantasies are your inalienable birthright. They are protected by your guaranteed right to privacy—is anything more private than your personal daydreams? I urge you to defend in every possible way your right to fantasize anything you like, whenever you like, in the privacy of your own imagination.

APPENDIX

A Cornucopia of Fantasies

When it comes to imagination, most of us fit into either of two categories: We have it—or we don't.

If we have an active imagination, and we've reached our twenties, we've already used it to create hundreds of sexual daydreams. We've learned to really love fantasizing all sorts of experiences. Inventing new fantasies is like having new sexual experiences—something we never tire of. Those of you who are imaginatively endowed, I offer the following fantasy situations to jump-start you into new realms of pleasure.

And, to those readers who are not so gifted, I particularly recommend this list. You'll find it especially useful by turning to those categories that excite you most. Little by little, explore related categories and see how well they work for you.

Remember: Sex is like life in general—what you get out of it depends on how much you put into it.

Finally, if you're gay and the fantasy is straight, or if you're straight and the fantasy is gay—*use your imagination.*

Vanilla Dreams

You're hiking through a woods and come upon a clearing and a pond. A beautiful woman comes out of the water naked and lies on a blanket to dry herself in the sun. You wait until she's asleep.

You check into a hotel room late one night and find a naked woman huddled in a dark corner of the balcony outside your room. She has just escaped from her cruel boyfriend in the next room by climbing around the divider, and will do anything you ask if you will just take her in.

Three young nurses live in the apartment across the hall from yours. One Saturday morning, the sexiest one knocks on your door. Seems her battery is dead. They all work the three-to-eleven shift, so there's no hurry. But if you would be kind enough to drive her to an auto parts store and install the battery, all three nurses would make it worth your while.

You're in a bar minding your own business when a small woman with a beautiful figure and submissive eyes stands next to you and says, "Tonight I'm my husband's slave, and he's told me I must do this." With that her hand drops to your crotch and she begins to fondle you. "Will you come home with me?" she asks, her eyes pleading.

You step out of the shower to find a stunningly beautiful woman whom you've never met leaning naked against the sink, one foot on the vanity top, exposing all her favors. She's your wife's birthday present to you.

She's young and has never seen a man naked before. When you drop your pants, she exclaims, "Oh, my God, it's so big!" Shyly, she does your bidding.

You've suffered a great loss. You've always been good friends and now she comforts you, pulling your head to her breast. While you remain passive, she nurtures you, undresses you, masturbates you.

The two of you are alone at a desolate beach. You strip nude, swim together, and then, with the waves lapping at your bodies you make love.

It's against your religion, your ethics, your marital vows for both of you, but your spouses are away. What started out as a little innocent petting has led to overwhelming lust, and now neither of you has the strength to resist.

You hardly know her. She tells you that she wants a baby but not a man, and she would use artificial insemination if she had the money. She wants you to screw her without foreplay while she pretends to be asleep.

You're a high school teacher. Babette isn't very bright, but she's very sexy. She comes to see you after school about getting a passing grade, which she hasn't earned. She makes it clear that she is willing to do anything, and has the experience.

You're a high school sophomore. After repeated complaints from teachers about your hyperactivity, you're sent to see the nurse. She's 23 years old, stacked and sophisticated. Locking the door behind you, she orders you to undress, fellates you to erection and has you screw her in order to dissipate your excess energy.

Through no effort on your part, she's fallen madly in love with you. You try to ignore her, but one night she corners you in an alley, unbuckles your belt and drops to her knees. "If it makes you happy," you say with a shrug, "go ahead and blow me."

She wears sweaters so low that you can practically see her nipples. She French kisses, fondles your erect dick in your pants, puts your hands on her breasts—but when it comes to relieving the tension, she says no. You twist her arm, and she agrees to do whatever you say.

She's your best friend's wife. She wants a baby, but he's infertile. She begs you to impregnate her, saying it was your friend's idea.

More than 100 women run a five-mile race. Some collapse from exhaustion along the way. Others, scraped and bloody, crawl across the finish line where, standing on a platform naked, you are first prize.

Your wife and her closest girlfriend think you're away for the weekend but you come home early to find them naked on the living room rug in each other's arms. They accept your ultimatum and allow you to share their pleasures.

You were sent an invitation to the just-concluded wedding. She has always loved you and you knew it, and in the confusion following the ceremonies, you lead her to the vacant chapel, lie her across the alter, lift her wedding gown over her head and screw her.

She tells you that she's a virgin, pleads with you not to rape her, but you strip her naked, hold her immobile, and, while licking the tears from her eyes, do the dastardly deed.

Sadistic fantasies

He's cute, but frail, and you can tell by his girlish mannerisms that he's been beaten and abused by lots of guys before now. So what difference does one more time make?

Late at night, you discover them making out on a park bench. First, you pummel him into unconsciousness. Then you strip her nude and make her lie across his body before screwing her.

You attend a slave auction. While others watch, you pat and pinch her naked body, fondle her breasts, use your fingers to determine the tightness of her vagina. When you discover that she's a virgin, you buy her and take her home to your bedroom immediately.

You keep him naked and half starved so that he isn't strong enough to resist. He's kept chained day and night in the dungeon, and brought up only for meals, baths, and to service you. He's eager to please, for only then is he fed.

Janet is only 18, and dressed in the gown for which she has spent every penny. You have promised to take her to a world film premier, but she ends up in your woodland hide-away, where she will remain your prisoner forever.

You are masturbating him very slowly. All the while you're impaling him as well. He understands that when he reaches orgasm you will strangle him. Yet, you can feel his sturdy phallus pulsating in your hand. You both know his end is near.

You have a stable of naked women whom you keep pregnant in order to breed your own farm workers.

You found her with another man and immediately moved to the country where she spends every day tied to a table nude, her legs spread, so that an endless stream of rednecks use her in every fashion, ejaculating all over her body.

In a jealous rage, he suspends his girl's secret lover from a rafter by his genitals, forces his legs apart by ropes fastened to the walls and impales him anally.

He has made her love him more than life itself, has taken her from her husband and family so that now she has only him. When she finishes fellating him, he will say goodbye to her forever.

After fondling his phallus to erection, they will hang him naked just to see if men really do ejaculate while being hanged. As the tension mounts, they masturbate.

She believes that you're taking her to your multi-media room in the basement. When she enters and you throw on the lights, she finds chains, whips, racks, and daggers.

A dozen young men volunteer to sacrifice themselves to the Goddess of the Volcano. One at a time, they stand naked at the rim masturbating. As they reach orgasm, they step off and plunge into the molten lava. Those who repent their decision are forcefully masturbated and hurled into the flames.

Your initiation into a motorcycle gang requires you to pick up a girl and bring her to a "party." She doesn't know that she will be the night's entertainment, servicing 15 guys in every imaginable way.

He has done nothing to you. Yet, you continue to whip him until he is a mass of welts and blood.

You're the high priest. She is the virgin sacrifice. She lies on the altar, her head back, and you impale her orally. She dies at the moment of your climax.

You capture a young nun, strip her and restrain her so that her head is over the side of the bed. You straddle her head and make her lick your genitals. She does so with enthusiasm.

Masochistic Fantasies
You're straight, but you look and act gay, and because of that dozens of guys have kicked and beaten you and then made you get them off. You thought John would be the exception, a best friend who wouldn't abuse you. But now that you're on an overnight camp-out together, you discover how wrong you were.

He's the only sex partner you've ever had. You love him. He asks you to prove it. His initiation into the fraternity requires that he produce someone who will service all the brothers sexually and in public. You say yes.

You're helplessly bound, your legs spread wide. He touches you tenderly, erotically, and you respond in breathless gasps. Still, there is that knife in his hand.

He's tied you naked to the hood of his auto and raced along the expressway at eighty miles an hour. Other drivers honk and wave, but no one seems concerned. Later, he will take you to the back woods of redneck country, where his friends will use your genitals for dart practice.

You're naked in a spike-lined cage. You've been injected with a powerful aphrodisiac, and you're in a frenzy of lust, but your hands have been tied behind your back, and the mouths and orifices that could bring you satisfaction are on the other side of the bars. You thrust into the nearest orifice, mindlessly tearing your body on the spikes.

You're a human mare at a breeding farm. Twice daily, while your breasts are being milked for commercial purposes, genitally superior young studs wearing sterilized condoms screw you.

You are being sacrificed to Moloch. The last thing you will feel is orgasm at the lips of the beautiful princess.

The thugs hang you by your wrists and whip you brutally with leather belts while they masturbate.

For kicks, a sadist ties you to a table and tightens a clear plastic bag around your neck so that he can watch your face and your phallus as you approach death. He releases the bag just as you're about to pass out, allows you a few gasps, and then repeats the process. When he takes hold of your penis and begins masturbating you, you realize the end is near.

You know that the men who are forcing you to serve them will never let you leave their hideout.

He makes you watch while he has sex with his new love and whispers of his undying affection.

You know he will leave you bruised and bloody, because you've been with him scores of times. Yet, you love his strength, his beauty, and even his tenderness, so, when he calls to invite you over, you say yes.

In a few hours you are to be executed. The warden will be the only witness. Who's to know of the tortures they now plan to inflict on your body for their sexual pleasures?

You've been raped and left naked at the side of the road. You flag down a trucker for help, but he, too, rapes you, and leaves you in the grass. One after another, motorists stop only to abuse you and drive on.

Your father and grandfather force you to serve them sexually while your brother looks on laughing and masturbating.

You're a young, attractive high school gym teacher. One day after class, several students corner you in the shower and have their way with you.

You're Saint Sebastian, hanging on a cross naked. Every eye is on your writhing body. As the first arrow pierces your abdomen, you feel no pain, only an erotic surge, as though being penetrated by a phallus. Soon you are erect, and as the final arrow pierces your flesh, you ejaculate.

You've been thrown nude from an airplane and are plunging toward earth. Your hands are tied to the ripcord of a parachute, and you can pull it, but a steel thread is fastened tightly around your genitals, the other end of it to the parachute. The sudden jerk of the inflated chute will sever your genitals. You imagine them landing on a table at a formal tea party.

It gives her pleasure to whip you, and touch lighted cigarettes to your body in front of an audience of feminists. When you're too weak to stand, she ties you to a rack and allows the audience to come up on stage one by one, squeeze your balls and stick needles into your flesh. You endure for love's sake.

You're the subject of a college biology seminar. Gagged and bound nude, you stare into the eyes of the professor who, standing between your legs, is about to expose the contents of your scrotum.

Exhibitionism/Voyeurism

From your hiding place in the woods, you see across a deep but narrow chasm (not more than 50 feet wide) a family having a picnic. They bow their heads to say grace, and when they glance up they discover you standing on the ledge naked, fondling your balls with one hand and beating off with the other. They stare in stunned disbelief until you ejaculate and retreat.

You're the star of a live sex show. The audience applauds as your huge penis grows erect. Suddenly, a man in the first row leaves his wife's side, comes up onto the stage, drops to his knees and fellates you.

You discover that, going to your attic and peering out the vent near the roof, you can see above the cafe curtains in your neighbor's bedroom and watch him perform all sorts of sexual tricks with his penis.

You *are* that neighbor, and secretly know you're being observed. You delight in spreading your legs wide apart and thrusting you hard phallus directly at your bedroom window.

You have a wooden privacy fence around your yard and enjoy walking nude in the grass while masturbating. You've spotted your neighbor's teenaged son watching you through a missing knothole and so now you put on shows especially for him.

While your neighbor's son is at school, you attach a mirror at the far end of the fence. He always comes to the knothole first thing after school, and you await with hard-on in hand. Sure enough, you spy him in the mirror, and to your delight, realize that he has not been just observing, but masturbating along with you.

One day, out of view of your young neighbor, you approach the knothole and suddenly thrust your penis through it. You hear a gasp on the other side, and then, after a moment, feel a wet mouth on your organ.

You've been hired to be the "model" at a women's clinic on how to sexually please men. You stand before the audience nude while the speaker demonstrates various techniques of arousal, including prostate massage.

A gay couple has moved into the apartment directly across the alley. Every night, you sit on your balcony in nothing but jogging shorts, pull out your penis and masturbate to orgasm. On the third night, while you're performing, both of your neighbors come out on their balcony and match you stroke for stroke.

You're wearing nothing but shorts when you slip into the girls' high school locker room. When they come in after class to shower, you're naked and erect. Their screams shoot you over the edge.

Although you're straight, you agree to dance nude at a gay bash for the right price. The audience of 20 is so incited by your performance that they all begin masturbating. To your surprise, you, too, sport an erection, and before long, you're the center of an orgy.

You're an electronics wizard, and manage to cut into the broadcast signal of the Family Channel. Suddenly the *Brady Bunch* is interrupted, and you watch yourself masturbate to orgasm on network TV.

Two girls and a boy find you sleeping nude in the

woods. They're intrigued by your sex organs and ask if they may play with them.

You ask your best friend if you can watch while he and his girlfriend have sex. He agrees, but only if you sit naked and masturbate at the same time.

You're sitting in a dimly lit bar. The music's loud, the smoke thick. A hand reaches from behind you and pulls down your zipper, slips into your trousers and pulls out your genitals. You try to appear casual in your conversation with the bartender as the anonymous hand masturbates you to orgasm.

A photographer pays you good money to pose nude. The poses he requests grow more and more erotic until finally he persuades you to masturbate on video tape.

Five finalists stand before you, the judge, in a Solo Sex Techniques Contest. You must judge the contestants on the attractiveness of their erect organs, the quality of their techniques and the degree of pleasure they have with their orgasms as measured by the force of their ejaculations, quantity of semen, moans, and facial contortions.

At the moment you reach orgasm, a friend opens the door and discovers you spurting.

Your college is very progressive. The trustees agree to allow a naked cheer leading squad. You stand proudly at the top of the pyramid, but the game never takes place, for your performance leads to a mass orgy.

Kinky

You lie in a large tub surrounded by water-filled balloons. They feel like the breasts of many women.

He's a large, friendly collie, and somehow you've turned him on sexually. He needs relief.

You drape a blanket over your front porch rail and sit naked behind it during rush hour. You return the waves of passing neighbors and even chat while masturbating not more than ten feet from them.

You check into a room on the twenty-fifth floor of a New York City hotel, throw open the window, and masturbate onto the crowd below.

You're vacationing in a country where the age of consent is fourteen. She asks if you would like to do it. You answer yes.

A stranger sitting next to you at the back of the bus makes polite conversation, then suddenly reaches over, unzips your pants, begins masturbating you. He bends and puts his lips around your penis. He asks nothing more of you than your semen.

It's New Year's Eve. You phone all of your single and lonely neighbors and invite them over for an orgy. They're grateful, and, as midnight approaches, they lavish you with attention.

You're a funeral director, and enjoy having sex with corpses.

You're the life-affirming version of Jack Kevorkian. Terminally ill people phone you for sex. While you're pleasuring them, they feel no pain and become content with their fate.

You smear your genitals with raw meat and offer them to a swarm of flies and mosquitoes.

Your favorite sex partner is your car. Your zipper comes down the moment your butt hits the seat, and everything keeps hanging out until you reach your destination. You've had orgasms in every seat, masturbated into the trunk and even screwed the grill, but your favorite is always the tailpipe.

He licks one of your arm pits while she licks the other. They take turns fondling and masturbating you.

You're a young teenager. He holds you so tightly in his arms while impaling you that you can hardly breathe. Still, you feel content and loved.

You love sky diving nude, especially if you can ejaculate before coming into view.

You've invented a machine that will massage your prostate, gently stroke your penis and suck your nipples at the same time. You love it so much that you're already planning a wedding.

You have hobbled a stallion by all four legs so that he can't move, and are fulfilling a life-long dream of jerking off a horse.

BIBLIOGRAPHY

CHAPTER I

1. Robert C. Sorensen, Ph.D., "Various Aspects of Masturbation by Teenage Boys and Girls," *Human Autoerotic Practices*, Manfred F. DeMartino, editor, Human Sciences Press, New York, 1979, p. 99

2. Manfred F. DeMartino, *Human Autoerotic Practices*, Human Sciences Press, New York, 1979, pp. 341-344

3. Harold Leitenberg, and Kris Henning, "Sexual Fantasy," *Psychology Bulletin*, May, 1995, p. 480

4. Ibid, pp. 480-481

5. Ibid, p. 482

6. Ibid, pp. 469-496

7. Sandra Byers, et. al., "Sexual Intrusive Thoughts of College Students," *Journal of Sex Research*, November, 1998, pp. 359-369

8. Paul Cameron, Ph.D., "Are Sexual Fantasies Common?" *Sexual Behavior*, March 1972, p. 7

9. Shere Hite, *The Hite Report on Male Sexuality*,

Alfred A. Knopf, New York, 1981, pp. 4, 94, 510

10. Robert J. Stoller, M.D., *Perversion, the Erotic Form of Hatred*, Pantheon Books, New York, 1995, p. xv

11. Helen Singer Kaplan, "Fiction and Fantasy: No-Nonsense Therapy for Six Sexual Malfunctions," *Psychology Today*, October, 1974, pp. 77-86

12. Warren Gadpaille, *The Cycles of Sex*, Scribner's, New York, 1975, pp. 289-290

CHAPTER II

1. Robert Bahr, "Life Beyond Boredom," *Kiwanis Magazine*, June/July, 1987, p. 31

2. Edrita Fried, "Masturbation in Adults," in R. E. L. Masters, editor, *Sexual Self-Stimulation*, Sherbourne Press, New York, 1967, p. 84

3. Ibid, pp. 90-91

4. N. Lukianowicz, M.D., "Imaginary Sexual Partner and Visual Masturbatory Fantasies," *Archives of General Psychiatry*, October, 1960, Volume III, pp. 429-449

5. Edrita Fried, op. cit., p. 94

6. Porter Davis, *Auto-Erotic Practices*, Mental Health Press, New York, 1949, p. 40

7. Albert Ellis, Ph.D., *Sex And The Liberated Man*, Lyle Stuart, New York, 1976

CHAPTER III

1. Walter Braun, M.D., *The Cruel and the Meek*, Lyle Stuart, New York, 1967, pp. 65-66

2. Gilbert Oakley, *Sex and Sadism Throughout the Ages*, Walton Press, London, 1965, p. 36

3. Ibid, p. 37

4. Ibid, p. 38

5. Ibid, pp. 38-39

6. R. E. L. Masters, *Sexual Self-Stimulation*, Sherbourne Press, Los Angeles, 1967, pp. 127-128

7. Walter Braun, M.D., op. cit., p. 96

8. Shere Hite, *The Hite Report on Male Sexuality*, Alfred A. Knopf, New York, 1981, pp. 744-746

9. Richard V. Yazmajian, "The Testes and Body Image Formation in Transvestitism," *Journal of the American Psychoanalytic Association*, April, 1966

10. Walter Braun, M.D., op. cit., p. 29

11. Richard Von Krafft-Ebing, *Psychopathia Sexualis*, Paperback Library, New York, 1965, pp. 84-87

CHAPTER IV

1. Leopold von Sacher-Masoch, *Venus in Furs*, Additions *Narcisse*, Paris, 1928, p. 10

2. Dominick A. Barbara, "Masochism in Love and Sex," *American Journal of Psychoanalysis,* Volume XXXIV (4), 1974, pp. 73-79

3. Theodor Reik, *Masochism in Modern Man*, Grove Press, New York, 1941, p. 6

4. Ibid

5. Arthur Koestler, *The Ghost in the Machine*, MacMillan, New York, 1967, p. 331

6. Earl Harper, *A Study in Masturbation Fantasies*, Powell Publications, 1970, p. 62

7. Ibid

8. Kerry Kelly Novick and Jack Novick, Ph.D., "The Essence of Masochism," in *The Psychoanalytic Study of the Child*, Yale University Press, New Haven, 1987, p. 356

9. Shere Hite, *The Hite Report on Male Sexuality*, Alfred A. Knopf, New York, 1961, p. 753

10. Leon Ferber, "Beating Fantasies," in *Masturbation from Infancy to Senescence*, Irwin M. Marcus M.D., John J. Francis, M.D., editors, International Universities Press, New York, 1975, p. 211

11. Ibid

12. Edward D. Joseph, *Beating Fantasies*, Universities Press, Inc., New York, 1965, p. 46

13. Hal Zucker, *The Ecstasy of Pain*, Brown Book Co., New York, 1962, p.28

14. Ibid, pp. 87-88

15. John Swain, *The Pleasures of the Torture Chamber*, Valhalla Books, New York, 1963, p. 197

16, Ibid, p. 196

17. Reik, op. cit., p. 349

18. Hite, op. cit., p. 749

19. Eugene E. Levitt, Ph.D., "Sadomasochism," *Sexual Behavior*, September, 1971, pp. 74-80

20. Reik, op. cit., pp. 41-42

21. Ibid, p. 56

22. Ibid, p. 157

23. Richard von Krafft-Ebing, *Psychopathia Sexualis*, Paperback Library, New York, 1965, p. 158

24. Marquis de Sade, *The One Hundred Twenty Days of Sodom*, Grove Press, New York, 1966. p. 194

25. John Money, et. al., *The Breathless Orgasm*, Prometheus, New York, 1991, pp. 91-92

26. Ibid, p. 94

27. Yukio Mishima, *Sun and Steel*, Grove Press, New York, 1970, p. 27

28. Reik, op. cit., p. 41

29. Kerry Kelly Novick and Jack Novick, op. cit., p. 354

30. Ibid, pp. 366-367

31. Dorothy Seiberling, "The Art-Martyr," *New York*, May 24, 1976, p. 64

32. Colin Wilson, *The Misfits*, Carroll & Graf, New York, 1988, p. 206

33. Wayne Shumaker, *Literature And The Irrational*, Washington Square Press, New York, 1966, p. 189

34. Reik, op. cit., p. 401

35. Ibid, p. 123

36. Ibid, p. 159

37. Walter Braun, M.D., *The Cruel and the Meek*, Lyle Stuart, New York, 1967, p. 46

CHAPTER V

1. Richard A. Posner, and Katharine B. Silbaugh, *A Guide to America's Sex Laws*, University of Chicago Press, Chicago, 1996, p. 83

CHAPTER VI

1. Paul Russell, *Boys of Life*, Plume, New York, 1991, p. 107

2. Onno Zwart, M.A., et. al., "Anal Sex and Gay Men: The Challenge of HIV and Beyond," *Journal of Psychology and Human Sexuality*, Volume X, No. 3/4, 1998, p. 95

3. Ibid, p. 99

4. David Lester, *Psychological Reports*, Volume 54, 1984, p. 606

CHAPTER VII

1. Robert Bahr, *The Virility Factor*, Putnam, New York, 1976, pp. 130-135

2. John P. Dececco, *Sex, Cells, and Same-Sex Desire: The Biology of Sexual Preference*, Harrington Park Press, New

York, 1995

    3. Robert J. Stoller, M.D., *Sex and Gender*, Science House, New York, 1968, pp. 5-7

    4. Harry Benjamin, M.D., *The Transsexual Phenomenon*, The Julian Press, New York, 1966, pp. 3-4

    5. William Masters, et. al., *Human Sexuality*, Third Edition, Scott, Foresman, Glenview, Illinois, 1988, p. 350

    6. Benjamin, op. cit., p. 50

    7. Gobind B. Lal, "Complimentarity of Human Sexes," in Harry Benjamin, M.D., *The Transsexual Phenomenon*, The Julian Press, New York, 1966, p. 168

CHAPTER VIII

    1. R. E. L. Masters, *Sexual Self-Stimulation*, Sherbourne Press, Los Angeles, 1967, pp. 134-135

    2. Robert J. Stoller, M.D., *Perversion, the Erotic Form of Hatred*, Pantheon, New York, 1975, p. 116

CHAPTER IX

    1. June M. Reinisch, Ph.D., *The Kinsey Institute New Report on Sex*, St. Martin's Press, New York, 1990, p. 92

    2. Marc H. Hollender, M.D., "Women's Use of Fantasy During Sexual Intercourse," in *Masturbation From Infancy to Senescence*, Erwin M. Marcus, M.D., and John J. Francis, M.D., editors, International Universities Press, New York, 1975, p. 325

    3. William H. Masters, M.D., et. al., *Human Sexuality*, Third Edition, Scott, Foresman, Boston, 1988, p. 349

    4. Hollender, op. cit., p. 31

    5. Ibid, p. 319

    6. Helen Singer Kaplan, M.D., *The New Sex Therapy*, Brunner/Mazel, New York, 1974, pp. 217-219

7. Rachel Miller, *The Bliss of Becoming One*, Rainbow Books, Highland City, Florida, 1996, p. 19

8. Ibid, p. 55

9. Brenda Love, *Encyclopedia of Unusual Sex Practices*, Barricade Books, Ft. Lee, New Jersey, 1992, pp. 102-103

CHAPTER X

1. Robert J. Stoller, M.D., *Perversion, the Erotic Form of Hatred*, Pantheon Books, New York ,1975, p. 115

2. Robert Bahr, Abridged and Published as "The Arms of Michael," *Indecent Exposures*, Factor Press, Mobile, Alabama, 1993, pp. 46-47

3. Walter Braun, M.D., *The Cruel and the Meek*, Lyle Stuart, Inc., New York, 1997, p. 65

4. Isidor Bernstein, "Integrative Aspects of Masturbation," in *Masturbation from Infancy to Senescence*, Erwin M. Marcus, M.D., et. al., editors, International Universities Press, New York, 1975, pp. 267-268

5. Kerry Kelly Novick, et. al., "The Essence of Masochism," in the *Psychoanalytic Study of the Child*, Yale University Press, New Haven, Connecticut, 1987, p. 375

6. Bernstein, op. cit., p. 69

7. J. K. Davidson and L. E. Hoffman, "Sexual Fantasies and Sexual Satisfaction: an Imperical Analysis of Erotic Thought," *Journal of Sex Research*, Volume 22, 1986, pp.184-205

8. Joseph LoPiccolo, Ph.D., et. al., "The Role of Masturbation in Treatment of Orgasmic Disfunction," in *Human Autoerotic Practices*, Manfred F. DeMartino, editor, The Human Sciences Press, 1979, pp. 289

9. Charles Silverstein and Edmund White, *The Joy of*

Gay Sex, Crown Publishers, New York, 1977, p. 128

10. Helen Singer Kaplan, M.D., *The New Sex Therapy,* Brunner/Mazel, New York, 1974, p. 270

11. Helen Singer Kaplan, M.D., "Orgastic Dysfunction," in *Human Autoerotic Practices,* Manford F. DeMartino, editor, Human Sciences Press, New York, 1979, p. 303

12. N. Lukianowicz, M.D., "Imaginary Sexual Partner and Visual Masturbatory Fantasies," *The Archives of General Psychiatry,* October, 1960, Volume III, pp. 429-449

13. Ibid

14. Ibid

15. Paul H. Gebhard, et. al., *Sex Offenders, an Analysis of Types,* Harper & Row, New York, 1965, pp. 503, 829

16. Ron Langevin, Reuben Lang, et. al., "The Prevalence of Sex Offenders With Deviant Fantasies," *The Journal of Interpersonal Violence,* June, 1998, p. 315

CHAPTER XII

1. Robert J. Stoller, *Perversion, the Erotic Form of Hatred,* Pantheon Books, New York, 1975, p. 115

2. Free Speech Coalition, 1997 White Paper

3. Eliva Haavio-Mannila, Ph.D., et. al.,"Correlates of Increased Sexual Satisfaction," *Archives of Sexual Behavior,* Volume XXVI. Number 4, 1997, pp. 399-419

4. Joseph LoPiccolo, et. al., "The Role of Masturbation in the Treatment of Orgasmic Dysfunction," in *Human Autoerotic Practices,* Manfred F. DeMartino, editor, Human Sciences Press, New York, 1979, p. 289

5. Walter Braun, M.D., *The Cruel and the Meek,* Lyle Stuart, 1967, p. 69

6. Ibid, p. 70

7. Ibid, pp. 70-71

8. F. M. Christensen, "Elicitation of Violence: The Evidence," in *Pornography*: *Private Right or Public Menace?* Robert M. Baird and Stewart E. Rosenbaum, editors, Prometheus Books, Amherst, New York, 1998, p. 261

9. Andrea Dworkin, "Against the Male Flood, Censorship, Pornography, Equality," *Pornography: Private Right or Public Menace?* Robert M. Baird and Stewart E. Rosenbaum, editors, Prometheus Books, Amherst, New York, 1998, p. 94

10. *Author's Guild Bulletin*, Spring, 1996